Y0-ART-373

THE TRISECTION PROBLEM

CLASSICS
IN MATHEMATICS EDUCATION

Volume 1: *The Pythagorean Proposition*
by Elisha Scott Loomis

Volume 2: *Number Stories of Long Ago*
by David Eugene Smith

Volume 3: *The Trisection Problem*
by Robert C. Yates

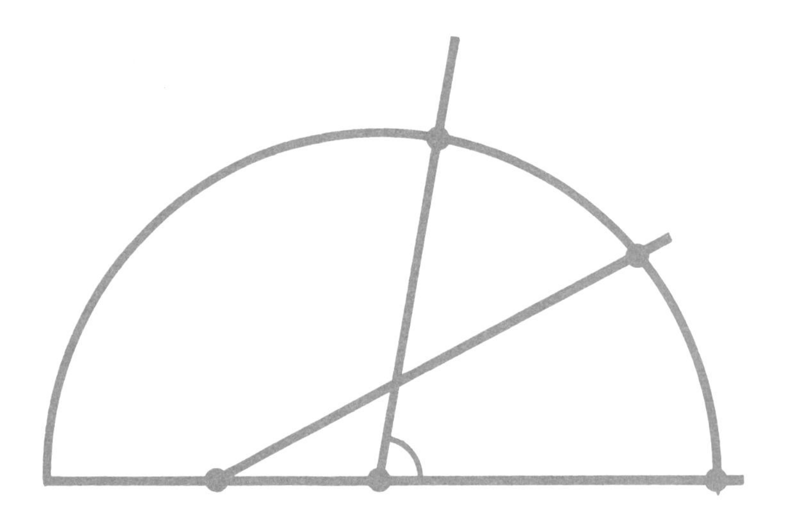

THE TRISECTION PROBLEM

Robert C. Yates

THE NATIONAL COUNCIL OF TEACHERS OF MATHEMATICS

Library of Congress Catalog Card Number: 77-176232

Printed in the United States of America

1971

FOREWORD

Some mathematical works of considerable vintage have a timeless quality about them. Like classics in any field, they still bring joy and guidance to the reader. Books of this kind, if no longer readily available, are being sought out by the National Council of Teachers of Mathematics, which has begun to publish a series of such classics. The present title is the third volume of the series.

The Trisection Problem was first published in 1942 by the Franklin Press, Inc., of Baton Rouge, Louisiana, when the author was teaching at Louisiana State University. A photo-lithoprint reproduction was issued in 1947 by Edwards Brothers, Inc., Lithoprinters, of Ann Arbor, Michigan. The present reprint edition has been similarly produced, by photo-offset, from a copy of the original publication. Except for providing new front matter, including a Table of Contents, a biographical sketch of the author, and this Foreword by way of explanation, no attempt has been made to modernize the book in any way. To do so would surely detract from, rather than add to, its value.

CONTENTS

ABOUT THE AUTHOR

Since I undertook to write this brief biographical sketch, letters have come to me from departments of mathematics where Bob Yates taught in the course of his career. One of these begins:

> "Bob was one of the most refreshing things that ever happened to this Department. His complete professionalism as a teacher and lecturer, his irrepressible wit and engaging social charm, plus the sadness, too, that we went through with him in the loss of his wife in childbirth shortly after he joined us, are all memories that are crystal clear to me. It is certainly a feather in his cap and a monument to his abilities that the NCTM intends to publish some of his work."[1]

This tribute expresses succinctly what those who knew the author well—his associates over a long period of time—thought about him as a man, a mathematician, and a teacher.

Robert Carl Yates was born in Falls Church, Virginia, on 10 March 1904. In 1924 he received a B.S. degree in civil engineering from Virginia Military Institute. This degree was followed by an A.B. degree in psychology and education from Washington and Lee University in 1926 and by the M.A. and Ph.D. degrees in mathematics and applied mathematics from Johns Hopkins University in 1928 and 1931.

While working on these later degrees Bob Yates was an instructor at Virginia Military Institute, the University of Maryland, and Johns Hopkins University. On completion of the Ph.D. degree, he accepted a position as assistant professor, in 1931, at the University of Maryland, where later he was promoted to associate professor. In 1939 he became associate professor of mathematics at Louisiana State University.

As a captain in the Army Reserves, Professor Yates reported to the United States Military Academy for active duty on 6 June 1942. Before

1. From a letter written by Colonel John S. B. Dick, professor of mathematics and head of the Department of Mathematics at the United States Military Academy.

leaving the Academy he rose to the rank of colonel and the title of associate professor of mathematics.

He left West Point in August 1954, when a reduction in the number of colonels was authorized at USMA, and accepted a position as professor of mathematics at Virginia Polytechnic Institute. In 1955 he became professor of mathematics and chairman of the department at the College of William and Mary. The last position he held was as one of the original professors at the University of South Florida, beginning in 1960. He went to this new institution as chairman of the Department of Mathematics, resigning the chairmanship in 1962 in order to devote more time to teaching, lecturing, and writing.

During his tour of duty at West Point, Dr. Yates spent many of his summers as a visiting professor. Among the institutions he served were Teachers College, Columbia University; Yeshiva University; and Johns Hopkins University.

Robert Yates was a man of many talents. Although he was trained in pure and applied mathematics, he became interested in the field of mathematics education rather early in his professional career. In both areas he built up a fine reputation as a lecturer and a writer. During his lifetime he had sixty-odd papers published in various research and mathematical-education journals, including the *Mathematics Teacher,* and in NCTM yearbooks. He also wrote five books dealing with various aspects of geometry, the calculus, and differential equations. From 1937 until he was called to active duty at West Point in 1942, he served on the editorial board, and as editor of one department, of the *National Mathematics Magazine.*

These were some of his professional achievements. His activities, however, were not limited to the world of mathematics. At VMI, where he was a member of the track squad, dramatics and journalism claimed some of his time. Music became a continuing resource. In later life his recreations included playing the piano as well as sailing, skating, and golf.

Dr. Yates, whose social fraternity was Kappa Alpha, was elected to two scientific honor societies: Gamma Alpha and Sigma Xi. Holding membership in the American Mathematical Society, the Mathematical Association of America, and the National Council of Teachers of Mathematics, he was at one period a governor of the MAA. He was also a member of the MAA's original ad hoc Committee on the Undergraduate Program in Mathematics (CUPM). In late 1961 he was selected by the Association of Higher Education as one of twenty-five "outstanding college and university educators in America today," and on 4 February 1962 he was featured on the ABC-TV program "Meet the Professor."

Dr. Yates had been interested in mathematics education before 1939.

However, when he came to Louisiana State University, his work in this field began to expand. Owing to his efforts, the Department of Mathematics and the College of Education made some important changes in the mathematical curriculum for the training of prospective secondary school teachers. One of the most important additions was six semester hours in geometry. Dr. Yates was given this course to teach, and for a text he used his first book, *Geometrical Tools*. From this beginning his interest and work in mathematics education increased, while he continued to lecture and write in the areas of pure and applied mathematics.

The atmosphere at West Point was quite a change for Dr. Yates. However, even here he continued his activities in mathematics education. One of his duties was to supervise and conduct courses in the techniques of teaching mathematics. These were courses designed for the groups of new instructors who joined the department staff annually; for most of the faculty at the Academy, then as now, were active-duty officers who came on a first or second tour of three to four years' duration. In performing this duty he was considered a superior instructor and also an excellent teacher of teachers.

After leaving the service Professor Yates continued his efforts to improve mathematics education. During the summers he taught in several different mathematics institutes, and he was a guest lecturer in many summer and academic-year institutes supported by the National Science Foundation. In earlier years he both taught and lectured in the grandfather of all institutes, the one developed by Professor W. W. Rankin at Duke University. In Virginia and later in Florida he served as a consultant to teachers of mathematics in various school districts. During the academic years 1961/62 and 1962/63 the University of South Florida was engaged in an experimental television program. Professor Yates was the television lecturer in the course materials developed through this program. As a result of this program as well as the MAA lectureship program for high schools, supported by the NSF, he traveled to all parts of Florida giving lectures and consulting with high school teachers.

Through all these activities Dr. Yates greatly enhanced the field of mathematics education. He built up a reputation as an outstanding lecturer with a pleasing, interest-provoking presentation and a rare ability to talk while illustrating his subject. Those who have heard him will long remember him and his great ability. Others will find that his writings show, somewhat vicariously, these same characteristics.

By his first wife, Naomi Sherman, who died in childbirth, he had three children. Robert Jefferson, the eldest, is now in business in California. Melinda Susan, the youngest, is now Mrs. Richard B. Shaw, the wife of a Missouri surgeon. Mrs. Shaw majored in mathematics at Mount Holyoke

College, and before getting married she worked for the American Telephone and Telegraph Company as a computer programmer and systems analyst. The second child is Daniel Sherman. He is following in his father's footsteps and is currently completing his doctorate in mathematics education at Florida State University.

Dr. Yates passed away on 18 December 1963 and was interred in Arlington National Cemetery.

HOUSTON T. KARNES

Louisiana State University

THE TRISECTION PROBLEM

Much of the history of mathematics is reflected in, or owes its origin to, the three problems of the ancients. The most elementary of these, and the one with the widest appeal, is that of trisecting the general angle.

Long considered a closed chapter by some, it is nonetheless a subject of constant investigation by others. Endowed with a strange will-o'-the-wisp character, it reappears perennially upon the pages of scientific journals and the newspapers, in discussions of the classroom and street corner. Academically, it serves as a medium through which the student is brought to an understanding of the nature and limitations of Euclidean geometry.

To that group of persons who found their first real interest in mathematics awakened by the problem of trisecting the angle is this little volume dedicated.

The Trisection Problem

CHAPTER I

THE PROBLEM

1. The Famous Three

In the history of mathematics there are three problems that have persisted with astounding vigor for over two thousand years. They are *Trisecting the Angle, Duplicating the Cube,* and *Squaring the Circle,* and because of their hardy existence they are now called Famous Problems. The bare problems themselves, stripped of all implications, seem hardly worth more than passing attention and yet, even today, an incredible amount of energy is expended in the search for solutions by some means or other. We cannot help but wonder why three such apparently simple mathematical issues should stand forth above all others. Statements of the problems can be made in the simplest of terms and no one need be terrified by the heavy terminology usually associated with mathematical questions. It is just this disarming simplicity, however, that invites one to make courageous attacks. Doctors, lawyers, butchers and bakers, young men and old men, amateur mathematicians and professional ones, the sane and the insane—people in all walks of life have been drawn to them only to be snared insidiously in a web of their own spinning or to open for themselves suddenly and unexpectedly a path down which they could look into new fields. These three problems, solidly impregnable to all approaches from the vantage of plane geometry, the medium of the ancient Greeks, served only to tantalize and tease the mathematician into devising new apparatus and theorems for their solution. Through this stimulus did much of our present structure of algebra and geometry grow.

Constant search over so long a period for solutions of the Three Problems has yielded amazingly fruitful discoveries, often hit upon by the sheerest accident, that have thrown light in a totally unsuspected manner upon far distant things. The Ellipse, Parabola, and

Hyperbola—sections formed from a cone by a cutting plane—are undoubtedly the most interesting and useful curves known. Without them we would be sore put to explain the heavens or to fire upon the hidden enemy or to peer into the habits of the microscopic world. It is said that these curves were discovered by Menæchmus in an ambitious attempt at the solution of the Three Problems. A further outgrowth was the development of that important field, the Theory of Equations. More indirectly, we find traces of their influence in the modern Group Theory, a doctrine of the highest importance to the physicist and chemist in their study of atomic structure and relativity theory. Little wonder then that these problems, to the credit of which so much mathematical activity is due, should now be classified as famous.

2. A Classical Game

The plane geometry of the ancient Greeks was a game to be played with simple equipment and governed by a rigid set of rules. The equipment consisted only of the *compasses* and an *unmarked straightedge*, indefinite in length. The rules, established and insisted upon by Plato,* were the postulates which allowed certain privileges in the use of the tools. These permitted:

1. The drawing of a straight line of indefinite length through two given distinct points;
2. The construction of a circle with center at a given point and passing through a second given point.

Indeed, it seems that a game built around such scanty outlay would be a disappointing affair. Nothing, however, could be farther from the truth. Probably the most fascinating game ever invented, it is awe-inspiring in its extent to the novice, and a thoroughly absorbing occupation to the expert.

Any geometry that was indulged in which did not adhere closely to the Platonian rules was condemned as unsportsmanlike and ill-befitting the ideal thoughts of the scholar and mathematician. This was the general opinion of the old classical school. All geometrical situations had to be met with only straightedge and compasses. But under their rules, these tools alone are incapable of producing solutions of the Three Problems. This fact, however, was not established until about 1800—two thousand years later. This statement is not surprising in view of the fact that it is necessary to pass beyond

*As rumor has it.

the confines of plane geometry in order to show that solutions cannot be found there. The mathematical structure needed to do this was a long time being developed and at first seemed to have nothing whatever to do with geometry.

3. *Trisection*

The first of the Three Problems, the trisection of a general angle, no doubt arose, so long ago that historians can find no record, in just the manner that we would propose it for ourselves today. We find it easy enough to *bisect* any angle whatever: with the compasses, locate a point which is equidistant from the sides of the given angle and then draw with the straightedge the line joining this point with the vertex of the angle. Success is easily won and we turn naturally to the division of the angle into three equal parts. After a variety of attempts restricted to the classical rules and tools the difficulties seem discouraging. We begin to suspect the existence of some underlying principles that block every move.

Hippias of Elis, who lived in the Fifth century B. C., was one of the first to attempt to solve the Trisection Problem. The very same obstacles presented themselves to thwart his efforts but, freeing himself from the Platonian rules, he devised a curve called the *Quadratrix*, to be discussed later, by means of which he was able to give an exact solution to the problem. But, we must understand, it was not achieved by straightedge and compasses alone.

Hippias was only one of the first to succumb to the charm of this perplexing question. A partial list of his followers will show you what a powerful pull it had upon the attention of the great and the near-great. Archimedes, Nicomedes, Pappus, Leonardo da Vinci, Dürer, Descartes, Ceva, Pascal, Huygens, Leibniz, Newton, Maclaurin, Mascheroni, Gauss, Steiner, Chasles, Sylvester, Kempe, Klein, Dickson—all of these, and hundreds more, attacked the problem directly or created the mathematics by which substantial advances could be made toward a full understanding of the situation.

4. *Statement of the Problem*

Let us express the requirements for solution of the Problem in analytical form.

(A) *Algebraic Formulation.* Given the angle $AOB=3\theta$, let us suppose one of the trisecting lines to be OT, Fig. 1, so that $TOB=\theta$. Select an arbitrary length on OA as the unit distance and draw the parallel AC to OT, meeting OB extended at C. Then angle $DCO=\theta$.

Now draw OD equal to the unit length so that triangle AOD is isosceles with base angles 2θ, angles DAO and AOT being equal since they are

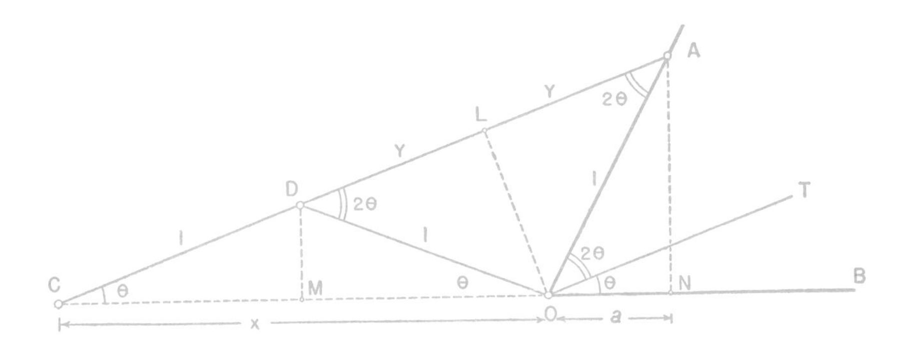

FIG. 1

alternate interior angles. It is evident, since angle ADO is the sum of the opposite interior angles of triangles DCO and angle $DCO=\theta$, that angle $DOC=\theta$. Therefore, triangle DCO is isosceles and $DC=DO=1$. Let x denote the distance OC, $2y$ the distance AD, and a the projection of OA upon the side OB. From similar triangles CMD, CNA, and CLO, all right triangles with equal angles at C, we find:

$$x/2=(x+a)/(1+2y)=(1+y)/x,$$

which give $\quad x^2=2+2y \quad \text{and} \quad 1+2y=2(x+a)/x.$

From these we eliminate y by substitution to obtain:

$$x^2-1=2(x+a)/x$$

or

$$\boxed{x^3-3x-2a=0} \tag{4.1}$$

This relation, as will be seen shortly, is fundamental to the problem and is called the Trisection Equation. It is a cubic equation with the term in x^2 missing.

(B) *Trigonometric Formulation.* A knowledge of trigonometry will produce the Trisection Equation in different fashion. In what follows we make use of the expression for the sine and cosine of the sum of two angles. We have:

$$\cos 3\theta=\cos(2\theta+\theta)=\cos 2\theta \cos \theta-\sin 2\theta \sin \theta.$$

This becomes, on replacing sin 2θ and cos 2θ by their equivalent values in terms of θ:

$$\cos 3\theta = (2\cos^2\theta - 1)\cos\theta - (2\cos\theta - 2\cos^3\theta), \qquad \text{or}$$

$$\cos 3\theta = 4\cos^3\theta - 3\cos\theta. \tag{4.2}$$

This expresses the cosine of a given angle in terms of the cosine of its third part. Looking again at Fig. 1:

$$x = 2\cos\theta \quad \text{and} \quad a = \cos 3\theta,$$

so that by making these replacements, (4.2) becomes:

$$a = x^3/2 - 3x/2,$$

or

$$x^3 - 3x - 2a = 0.$$

Note, before passing on, that no matter what angle is given, the corresponding value of a lies between $+1$ and -1 while that of x lies between $+2$ and -2.

Since we may drop the perpendicular from A upon OB and thus determine a, then we may think of this quantity as being *given* with the angle AOB. If the point C, or its distance x along OB, can be determined, the problem is at once solved by connecting C to A and then constructing the trisecting parallel OT. Thus we see that the *geometrical* solution of the problem is entirely equivalent to the *algebraic* solution of the corresponding Trisection Equation.

5. *Constructibility*

We may now restate the proposal in a different way: *Is it possible, for all values of a, to find by a straightedge and compasses construction a root x of the Trisection Equation?* The answer, suspected for so long, that it is not always possible is now definitely established.

Any construction which depends on the location of points by means of the straightedge and compasses is a permissible one under the rules of plane geometry. To conserve space we shall use the word *constructible* for the operations that can be performed with these tools. Since the Trisection Problem has now been put upon an algebraic footing, we must see how these operations appear in algebraic form. For, it is only through this medium that we can determine the character of the solution we seek.

(A) *Algebraic Equivalence of Constructibility.* If we are given two line segments, a and b, these segments can be added, subtracted, multiplied, and divided geometrically, using only straightedge and compasses. These operations on the given quantities are called *rational.* The first two need no explanation and are evident from the meanings of the words *sum* and *difference.* The multiplication of a and b is effected by drawing the line PQ, Fig. 2A, at any angle with PR and constructing the parallel line to produce similar triangles as

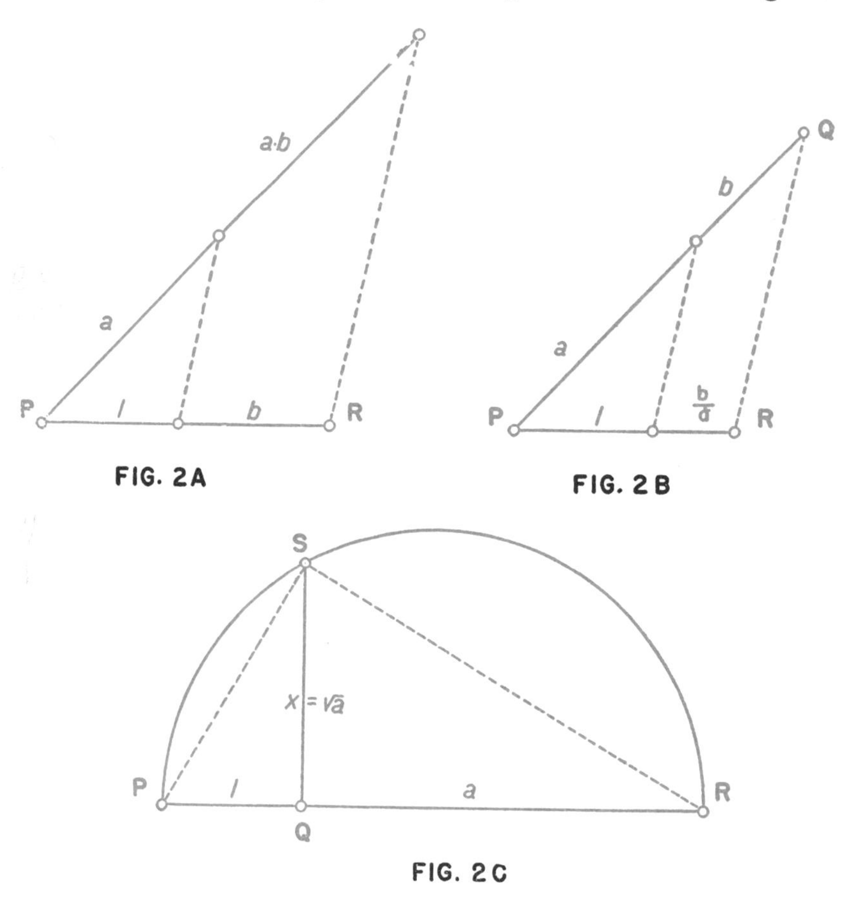

FIG. 2A

FIG. 2B

FIG. 2C

shown. Since a and b represent the *ratio* of segment length to unit length, the unit is given with a and b. Division of the segments, b/a, is similar to multiplication and should be obvious from Fig. 2B. The extraction of a root of a quantity is called an *irrational* operation. The *square root* of a line segment, a, may be constructed by drawing the semicircle with $(1+a)$ as a diameter and erecting the perpendicular at the joint of the segment and the unit distance. It should not be difficult to see from the two similar right triangles the proportion: $1/x = x/a$, and thus $x = \sqrt{a}$.

We shall presently show that these five algebraic operations are the only ones that admit construction by straightedge and compasses. Combinations of these, however, can be built up step by step to produce very complicated constructions. For example,

(1) $a+b\sqrt{c}$ (2) $\sqrt{a+\sqrt{b+\sqrt{c}}}$

(3) $(a+\sqrt{b})/(c+\sqrt{d})$ (4) $\sqrt{a}+\sqrt{(b+\sqrt{c})}$

are all constructible if the quantities a, b, c, d are given lengths and no imaginaries appear. Thus, for (2) we would first take the square root of c, then add b, then take the square root of the result, then add a, and finally take the square root of that result—all accomplished by straightedge and compasses as shown in Figure 2.

Generally, such expressions are called *quadratic irrationalities of order n*, where n is the least possible number of superimposed square root radicals. Number (2), for instance, is of order 3. Complicated as these irrational quantities appear, it will be noticed that they involve nothing more than a series of square roots of constructible lengths and they are, therefore, themselves constructible. We shall use a general symbol to represent all of them:

$$A+B\sqrt{C},$$

where A, B, C are constructible quantities and, generally, $\sqrt{C}$ is a quadratic irrationality of higher order than A and B.

Numbers of this sort may be roots of equations of much higher degree than the second—equations whose coefficients are either the given lengths or rational functions of them. Let us take a single illustration from the preceding group. If we set, for (3):

$$x=(a+\sqrt{b})/(c+\sqrt{d}),$$

and square, we have:

$$c^2x^2-2acx+a^2=b-2x\sqrt{(bd)}+dx^2.$$

Collecting and squaring again to remove the radical $\sqrt{(bd)}$:

$$(c^2-d)^2x^4-4ac(c^2-d)x^3+(6a^2c^2-2bc^2-2a^2d-2bd)x^2$$
$$-4(a^2-b)acx+(a^2-b)^2=0,$$

an equation of fourth degree in x whose coefficients are rational functions of a, b, c, and d.

We shall now prove that the rational operations of addition, subtraction, multiplication, and division, together with the irrational operation of extraction of square roots are the only ones possible by straightedge and compasses. To this end we transfer to analysis and use the algebraic interpretation of these geometrical elements.

All constructions of plane geometry are but the location of points either as the intersection of two lines, a line and a circle, or two circles.

I. Two given or constructed lines are represented by the equations

$$a_1x+b_1y+c_1=0$$

$$a_2x+b_2y+c_2=0$$

where the coefficients are geometrical lengths either given to start with or determined at some stage in the construction. These lines intersect in the point whose coordinates are the simultaneous solution of their equations, that is, in

$$x=(b_1c_2-b_2c_1)/(a_1b_2-a_2b_1), \quad y=(a_1c_2-a_2c_1)/(a_1b_2-a_2b_1).$$

These numbers are evidently rational functions of the coefficients in the equations of the lines. Thus the manipulation of the straightedge leads to no operation other than addition, subtraction, multiplication, and division of lengths.

II. The line $ax+by+c=0$

meets the circle $(x-h)^2+(y-k)^2=r^2$

in points whose abscissas are given by

$$(a^2+b^2)x^2+2(ac-hb^2+abk)x+c^2+2bck+(h^2+k^2-r^2)b^2=0,$$

or

$$Ax^2+Bx+C=0,$$

where the coefficients A, B, C are clearly rational functions of the quantities a, b, c and h, k, r. The solutions of this quadratic are

$$x=(-B\pm\sqrt{B^2-4AC})/2A,$$

quantities which involve, in addition to the operations mentioned in I, nothing further than the constructible irrationality $\sqrt{B^2-4AC}$.*

III. The intersections of two circles are the same as the intersections of their common chord and one of the circles. Thus, since the coefficients in the equation of the chord are rational functions of those in the equations of the circles, this case reduces immediately to II. Accordingly,

The straightedge and compasses together are capable of making only those geometrical constructions which are algebraically

*If the quantity B^2-4AC is negative, the roots are imaginary and there is no question of constructibility since the line and circle do not meet.

equivalent to a finite number of the operations of addition, subtraction, multiplication, division and the extraction of real square roots involving the given lengths.

6. The Impossible

In order to determine the impossiblity of trisection of the general angle, it suffices to give but a single example. Returning to the Trisection Equation, we shall discuss the situation for the particular angle $AOB=60°$. For this the projection value $a=\cos 60°=1/2$ produces the corresponding equation:

$$x^3-3x-1=0. \tag{6.1}$$

The question that must be decided is whether or not this equation has constructible roots of the sort described in the preceding pages. If not, then trisection is not always possible by straightedge and compasses. The argument is a bit involved, to be sure, but the end in view is worth the effort.

In order to proceed without interruption, we shall dispose of a necessary preliminary consideration. If x_1, x_2, x_3 are the roots of (6.1) we may write the equation as

$$(x-x_1)(x-x_2)(x-x_3)=0,$$

or

$$x^3-(x_1+x_2+x_3)x^2+(x_2x_3+x_3x_1+x_1x_2)x-x_1x_2x_3=0.$$

This, however, is identical with

$$x^3-3x-1=0.$$

It is evident on comparing these two forms that the sum of the roots of equation (6.1) is zero. That is, since the term in x^2 is missing, its coefficients must be zero. Thus

$$x_1+x_2+x_3=0. \tag{6.2}$$

(A) We shall first prove that *(6.1) does not have a rational root.* If we assume that it does, we are led to a contradiction, as follows:

Let $x=A/B$, where A,B are integers with no common factor other than 1. Then from (6.1): $(A/B)^3-3(A/B)=1$, which may be written in either of the forms:

$$3A+B=A(A/B)^2 \quad \text{or} \quad A^2-3B^2=B^2(B/A).$$

Now, since A and B are both integers, the left hand member of each of these equations is an integer. Accordingly, the right hand members must be integers and, since A and B have no common factors other than 1, the only possibility is that A and B have either of the values $+1$ or -1. That is, $x=\pm1$. But this is impossible for neither

$+1$ nor -1 satisfies (6.1). This establishes the statement that $x^3-3x-1=0$ has no rational root.

(B) If (6.1) has a constructible root of the sort $x_1=A+B\sqrt{C}$ where A and B are constructible irrationalities of lower order than $\sqrt{C}$, then on substituting in (6.1) we have:

$$(A+B\sqrt{C})^3-3(A+B\sqrt{C})-1=0,$$

or

$$(A^3+3AB^2C-3A-1)+(3AB+B^3C-3B)\sqrt{C}=0.$$

The only condition under which this can exist is that both quantities in the parentheses be zero. But this implies something further. Since the substitution of $(A-B\sqrt{C})$ produces the same equation except for a change in sign between the parentheses, we are apparently in possession of a second root: $x_2=A-B\sqrt{C}$. But, from (6.2) the three roots have zero for their sum; that is,

$$x_1+x_2+x_3=A+B\sqrt{C}+A-B\sqrt{C}+x_3=0,$$

or

$$x_3=-2A.$$

If, as we supposed, A is a constructible irrationality it must be of the sort, $L+M\sqrt{N}$ with $\sqrt{N}$ of higher order than either L or M but yet of lower order than $\sqrt{C}$. A repetition of the preceding argument applies here and forces us to admit the existence of a root whose irrationality is of the same order as L. Thus we are led from link to link down this chain of reason until we find the only constructible root that this equation *might* have is a rational number. But we demonstrated in (A) that it did not have such a root. Therefore, equation (6.1) has no constructible root and

60° cannot be trisected by straightedge and compasses.

7. *The Possible*

From the preceding discussions it is evident that certain angles do admit of trisection by straightedge and compasses. In fact, if the Trisection Equation

(7.1) $$x^3-3x-2a=0$$

can be factored into the form:

(7.2) $$(x+r)(x^2+sx+t)=0$$

where r, s, t are constructible coefficients, then the angle whose cosine is a can be trisected by these means. Since (7.1) and (7.2) are here identical, we may equate their coefficients, having:

$$r=-s, \quad t=r^2-3, \quad rt=-2a,$$

and the three roots of (7.2) may be written as:

$$x_1 = -r; \quad x_2 = (1/2)\,(r + \sqrt{3}\sqrt{1+2a/r}); \quad x_3 = (1/2)\,(r - \sqrt{3}\sqrt{1+2a/r}).$$

To illustrate such a possibility, consider the given angle $AOB = 54°$ whose cosine is $(1/4)\sqrt{(10-2\sqrt{5})}$. The corresponding Trisection Equation is therefore

$$x^3 - 3x - (1/2)\sqrt{(10-2\sqrt{5})} = 0,$$

which can be factored into the forms:

$$[x - (1/4)(\sqrt{5}+1)\sqrt{10-2\sqrt{5}}] = 0,$$

and

$$[x^2 + (x/4)(\sqrt{5}+1)\sqrt{10-2\sqrt{5}} + (\sqrt{5}-1)/2] = 0.$$

Notice that all coefficients, complicated as they are, are constructible and all roots are consequently constructible. Thus 54° can be trisected, or, which is the same thing, 18° can be constructed by straightedge and compasses.

The *discriminant*, D, of a cubic equation is an expression which indicates the character of its roots. For the Trisection Equation this discriminant is the quantity:

$$D = 108(1 - a^2).$$

Now, since a cannot be greater than 1, D is always positive and this assures us that all three roots of the equation are real numbers. Why should there be three when only one is all that is necessary to be determined for a given angle? The answer is found in realizing that the quantity a is not only the cosine of the given angle, 3θ, but also of $(360° + 3\theta)$ and of $(720° + 3\theta)$. Accordingly, the Trisection Equation delivers to us a root which determines the trisection of the given angle and two further "induced" roots corresponding to the angles $(120° + \theta)$ and $(240° + \theta)$. Thus for $3\theta = 90°$, $a = \cos 90° = 0$, and the Trisection Equation $x^3 - 3x = 0$ produces the three roots: $+\sqrt{3}$, $-\sqrt{3}$, and 0. The first of these values corresponds to the third part, 30°, of the given angle. The two remaining values give constructions for 150° and 270° as the third parts of the two induced angles.

Some Trisection Equations belonging to familiar angles which fall under the "possible" case are listed in the accompanying table:

AOB	$a=\cos(AOB)$	Trisection Equation	Roots
0°	1	$x^3-3x-2=0$	$-1, -1, 2$
45°	$\sqrt{2}/2$	$x^3-3x-\sqrt{2}=0$	$-\sqrt{2}, (\sqrt{2}/2)(1\pm\sqrt{3})$
72°	$(\sqrt{5}-1)/4$	$x^3-3x-(\sqrt{5}-1)/2=0$	$-2/(\sqrt{5}-1), 1/(\sqrt{5}-1)\pm\sqrt{\frac{15-6\sqrt{5}}{2(3-\sqrt{5})}}$
90°	0	$x^3-3x=0$	$0, +\sqrt{3}, -\sqrt{3}$
180°	-1	$x^3-3x+2=0$	$1, 1, -2$

Since we can trisect 72° and can bisect *any* angle, it follows that an angle of 3° is constructible. On the other hand, angles of 1° and 2° are not constructible for,* otherwise, we would be able to trisect 60°. It is somewhat startling to realize that the unit of angular measure we have used with so much familiarity cannot be constructed with straightedge and compasses.

8. *Other Criteria*

Although it is impossible to give a simple criterion to apply to all angles, the following discussion leads to rules that produce an infinitude of possibilities.

(A) If n is a given integer *not a multiple of 3*, then the equation

$$n \cdot b + 3 \cdot c = 1 \tag{8.1}$$

can always be satisfied by finding particular integer values for b and c. Thus, for example, $4b+3c=1$ is satisfied by $b=4$, $c=-5$; or $b=-5$, $c=7$; etc.; $-13b+3c=1$ by $b=2$, $c=9$; or by $b=-1$, $c=-4$. Multiplying (8.1) throughout by $(360°/3n)$, we have:

$$b(120°)+c(360°/n)=(1/3)(360°/n). \tag{8.2}$$

Now if the given angle AOB is of this type, $360°/n$, (18° for example) then (8.2) may be written (reversing the order):

$$AOB/3=c(AOB)+b(120°).$$

The angle 120° is itself constructible and we can always find integers b and c to satisfy this last equation. Thus, to construct $AOB/3$, we need only multiply the given angle by c, the angle 120° by b, and add

*Trisection of 60° followed by two bisections would produce an angle of 5°. The angle 2° results in constructing the difference 5° − 3°.

the result—all of which are possible constructions. It should be clear then that

If $AOB=360°/n$, where n is an integer not divisible by 3, then AOB admits of trisection by straightedge and compasses.

Obviously, $k(360°/n)$ is an angle in the same class if k is an integer.

(B) Suppose now that $AOB=360°/n$ where n is a multiple of 3, say $n=3^r \cdot m$ where 3^r contains all the factors 3, and m does not contain any. Then, as in the preceding, two integers b and c can be found such that

$$mb+3c=1$$

is satisfied. Multiplying this last equation through by $(360°/3n)$, we obtain:

$$mb(360°/3n)+c(360°/n)=(1/3)(360°/n).$$

In the first term, however, $m/n=1/3^r$, and thus

$$b(120°/3^r)+c(360°/n)=(1/3)(360°/n)$$

or
$$AOB/3=c(AOB)+2b(60°/3^r).$$

Now since r is a positive integer, the last term in the right member is either 20° or some repeated trisection of 60°. We have shown that 60° cannot be trisected by straightedge and compasses and it follows that $60°/3^r$ is not a constructible angle. Accordingly, $AOB/3$ is not constructible in this case and a companion rule to the preceding one is established:

If $AOB=360°/n$, where n is an integer divisible by 3, then AOB cannot be trisected by straightedge and compasses.

Another set of each class may be determined by the two following rules:

If p and q are integers and p is numerically less than q then it is possible to trisect by straightedge and compasses any angle whose cosine is

$$a=(p^3-3pq^2)/2q^3.$$

For, the corresponding Trisection Equation:

$$x^3-3x-(p^3-3pq^2)/q^3=0$$

is obviously satisfied if $x=p/q$, and this root is constructible. An example is furnished by the values $p=-1$, $q=3$. For these,

$\cos(AOB) = 13/27$ and AOB is approximately $61°13'$. On the other hand,

If the cosine of the given angle is p/q, where p and q are integers without common factors and q is greater than 1 but not the multiple of a cube, then it is impossible to trisect this angle by straightedge and compasses.

9. *Regular Polygons*

The general question of trisection enters into the study of the possibility of constructing regular polygons. Those of three, four, five, six, ten, and fifteen sides, for example, are constructible by straightedge and compasses, a fact well known to the ancient Greeks. But the polygons of seven, nine, eleven sides cannot be so constructed. This fact, like the proof of the impossibility of general trisection, was also late in being established. The ennagon, or 9-sided polygon, has the central angle of 40° subtended by each side and we have seen that this angle is not constructible. The construction of the 7-sided polygon depends on an equation of the third degree which can be shown, by a treatment similar to that of Paragraph 6, to contain no constructible roots. Gauss was the first to give a general constructibility rule for all regular polygons thus bringing to light some possibilities that were never dreamed of up to his time. Among the constructible ones were found the polygons of 17, 257, and even 65,536 sides. Unfortunately, the scope of this book does not permit us to wander down this enchanting path.

CHAPTER II

SOLUTIONS BY MEANS OF CURVES

From the very beginning, keen sighted persons suspected the impossibility of a solution of the Trisection Problem through the medium of straight lines and circles and looked about for other means to turn the trick. Since these two curves, the line and circle, were found insufficient, one person after another began to devise new and more complex curves, thus of course breaking the rules of the game as laid down by Plato. Many of these curves did offer solutions to the problem and, in addition, played important roles in other fields of mathematics and physics. For these reasons, they deserve a prominent place in our discussion. The drawing of these curves called for more complicated tools than the simple straightedge and compasses and their description forms a part of the subject of the next chapter.

1. *The Quadratrix*

The Quadratrix, invented by Hippias in an attempt to trisect the angle and square the circle, is formed in the following fashion. In Fig. 3, COB is a quadrant of the unit circle. The point D travels along the line from O to C at a constant rate. In the same interval of time, the point E moves from B to C along the arc, also at a constant rate. The horizontal line through D meets OE in P. The path described by P is the Quadratrix.

It is evident from this definition that the ratio of the lengths of any two arcs BE and BA is the same as the ratio of their corresponding segments on OC. That is,

$$OD/OF = BE/BA = \theta/\phi. \tag{1.1}$$

Having by some means drawn the curve, if $AOB = \phi$ is the angle to be trisected, it is necessary only to take $OD = (1/3)OF$, in the manner of Fig. 2. Thus from (1.1):

$$(1/3)(OF/OF) = \theta/\phi,$$

or

$$\theta = \phi/3.$$

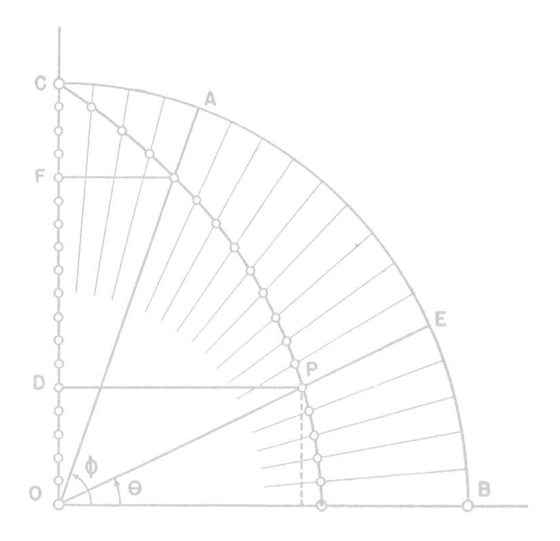

FIG. 3

The rectangular equation of the curve may be obtained as follows. Take OB and OC as the positive X and Y axes and let the coordinates of P be (x,y). Then since

$$OD/OC=\theta/(\pi/2), \quad x=(OP)\cos\theta, \quad OC=1, \quad OD=y,$$

we have:
$$x=y\cot\theta \quad \text{and} \quad y=2\theta/\pi.$$

These form the *parametric* equations of the Quadratrix and the *rectangular* equation results from eliminating θ:

$$\boxed{y=x\cdot\tan(\pi y/2)}$$

The reader familiar with indeterminate forms will find that the curve strikes the line OB at a point $2/\pi$ units distant from O.

2. *The Conchoid*

The Conchoid, designed by Nicomedes about 200 B. C., was used to obtain a solution of the Trisection Problem by Pappus five centuries

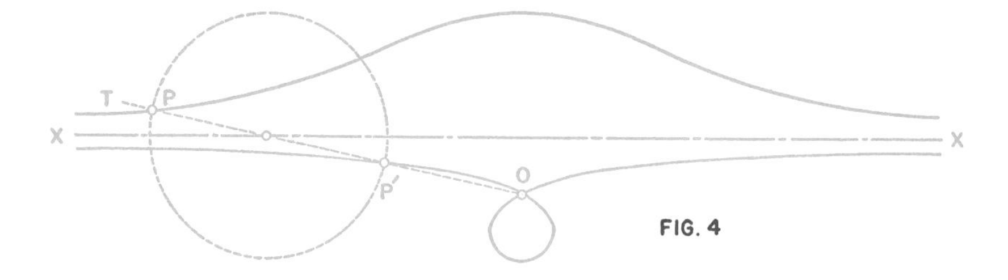

FIG. 4

later. It is formed in a very simple way. A circle moves with its center always on a fixed line XX. Through its center and also through a fixed point O, not on the line, passes the line OT. The path of the intersections P and P' of this line with the circle is the Conchoid. There are thus two branches of the curve, both having the line XX as an asymptote.

Unlike the Quadratrix, which, once drawn, can be used to trisect any given angle immediately, a fresh Conchoid must be constructed

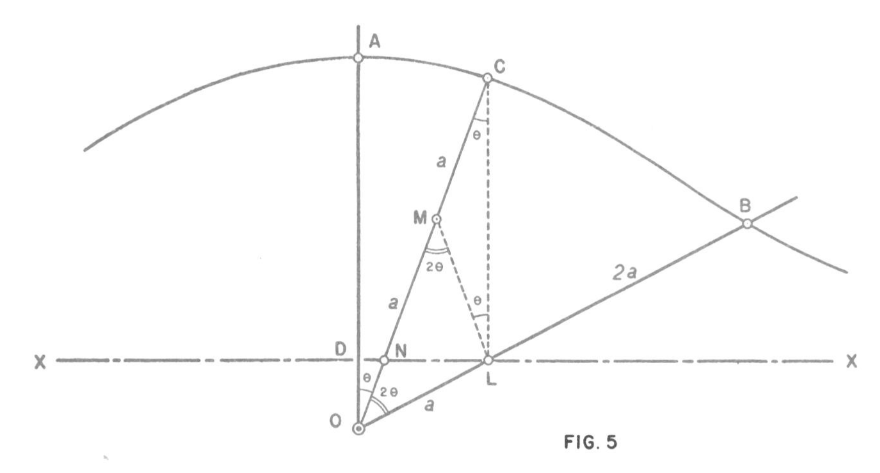

FIG. 5

for each new angle. Suppose it is required to trisect AOB, Fig. 5. Place the angle with vertex at O and draw the perpendicular line XX, cutting OB at L so that $OL=a$, the projection value: $\cos(AOB)$. Using $2a$ as the radius of the generating circle, draw the Conchoid ACB. At L construct the parallel to OA which will meet the curve at C. The line OC then trisects AOB. The proof of this is direct:

Let angle $AOC=LCO=\theta$. Now since $CN=2a$ (by definition of the curve) and CLN is a right angle, then the segment from the mid-point M of CN to the right-angled vertex L is of length a. Thus triangles CML and MLO are both isosceles. Accordingly,

$$\angle AOC=\angle OCL=\angle MLC=\theta.$$

But $\angle OML=2\theta$, since it is the exterior angle of triangle CML. Thus

$$\angle MOL=2\theta$$

and the angle AOB is trisected by OC.

A *polar* equation of the curve may be derived directly from the definition by selecting OA in Fig. 5 as the polar axis and O as the pole. We have $OC=r$ and angle $AOC=\theta$, where r and θ are now understood to be variables. If we denote the distance OD by b, we have from the right triangle ODN:

$$\cos\Theta = b/ON \quad \text{or} \quad ON = b/\cos\Theta.$$

Thus

$$\boxed{r = b/\cos\Theta + 2a}$$

is the polar equation of the upper branch.

Using XX and OA as X and Y axes respectively, the rectangular equation results from substituting $r = \sqrt{(x^2+y^2)}$ and $\cos\Theta = y/\sqrt{(x^2+y^2)}$ in the preceding polar equation. We find, after squaring:

$$\boxed{(x^2+y^2)(y-b)^2 = 4a^2y^2}$$

(The reader will find this interesting shell-shaped curve quite easy to construct. If 60° be the given angle, the corresponding Conchoid has $a = \cos 60° = 1/2$ and $b = a \cdot \cos 60° = 1/4$).

A word of caution should be made here against a possible misunderstanding. Although points on the curve may be found by straightedge and compasses, the *continuous* description is entirely beyond the possibilities of these instruments.

3. *The Hyperbola*

In solving the Trisection Equation, Pappus, about 300 A. D., made use of some properties of conic sections that were well known at that time. His method of trisection [**39**]* is essentially this: a unit circle is described with center at the vertex of the given angle AOB and the bisector OC constructed. A point P is allowed to move so that its distance from B is always *twice* its distance from the bisector OC. In this fashion P traces out a branch of an Hyperbola with the line OC as the *directrix* and the point B as *focus*. This branch is reflected in OC so that P' corresponds to P.

The points of intersection of the unit circle and the Hyperbola are trisecting points of the arc $AP'PB$. For, if $PQ = x = P'Q$, then $PB = P'A = 2x$ and the three isosceles triangles AOP', $P'OP$, and POB are congruent to each other with equal angles at their common vertex O.

To derive the rectangular equation of the curve, let AB and OC represent the X and Y axes. If we denote by $2c$ the distance AB, then B has the coordinates $(c,0)$ and we need only express in symbols

*Such bracketed numbers refer to items in the Bibliography.

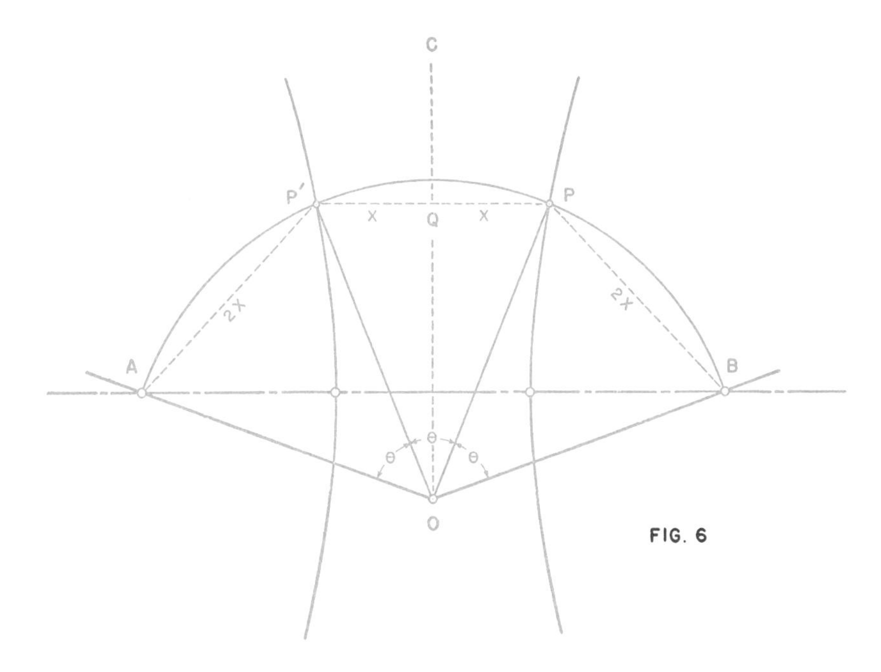

FIG. 6

the requirement that the distance PB must at all times be twice the distance PQ. That is, if the coordinates of P are (x,y):

$$\sqrt{(x-c)^2+y^2}=2x$$

or

$$\boxed{y^2-3x^2-2cx+c^2=0.}$$

The location of the trisecting point P requires the simultaneous solution of this equation and that of the circle, which is itself of the second degree. This gives rise to an equation of the fourth degree, the roots of which are the coordinates of P together with those of trisecting points for induced angles.

4. *The Limaçon*

The Limaçon, invented by Pascal about 1650, was later found to have trisecting possibilities. It is defined in a manner similar to the Conchoid: A point F is selected, Fig. 7, upon a fixed circle of unit radius. The movable line FA, which passes always through F, intersects the circle at P. The point A on the line at a constant distance b from P describes the curve.

The polar equation of the curve may be derived by taking the diameter FB as polar axis and F as pole. A then will have the coordinates (r,θ). Angle FPB is inscribed to the semicircle and is accordingly a right angle. Thus $FP=2\cos\theta$. Directly then,

$$\boxed{r=2\cos\theta+b}$$

is the equation of the path of A. Replacing r by $\sqrt{(x^2+y^2)}$ and $\cos\theta$ by $x/\sqrt{(x^2+y^2)}$ produces the rectangular equation:

$$\boxed{(x^2+y^2-2x)^2=b^2(x^2+y^2).}$$

Thus the Limaçon is a curve of the fourth degree.

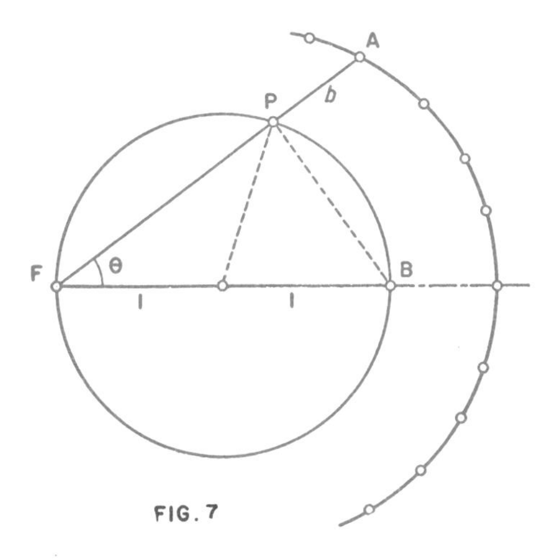

FIG. 7

The special value, $b=1$, is selected in order to utilize the curve as a trisector. Place the given angle, Fig. 8, with vertex at O, the center of the unit circle, and one side along its diameter FB. The other side will strike the Limaçon at A. Draw AF. Then the line through O parallel to AF trisects AOB. The proof follows: We have by construction:

$$AP=PO=FO=1,$$

so that triangles FOP and OPA are isosceles. Thus, if angle $OFP=\theta$,

$$\angle OPF=\theta \quad \text{and} \quad \angle POA=\angle PAO=\theta/2.$$

But $\angle BOP=2\theta$ since it is the exterior angle of triangle OFP.

Accordingly, $\angle AOB=\angle BOP-\angle AOP=2\theta-\theta/2=3\theta/2$,

and thus $$\angle PAO=\angle AOB/3.$$

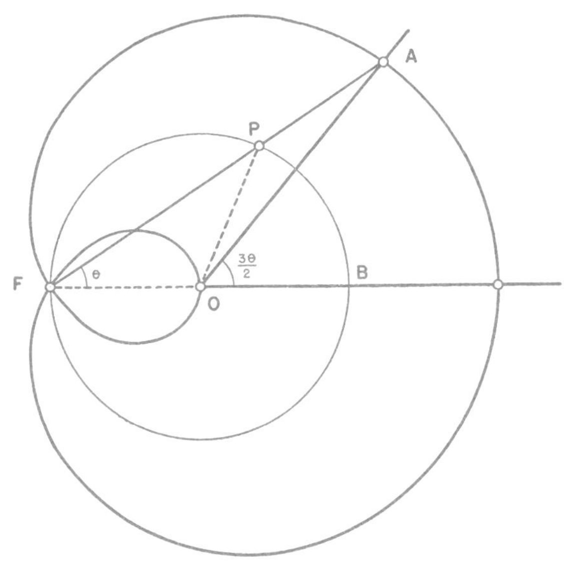

FIG. 8

There are three types of Limaçon which will be interesting to sketch by taking, for example, $b=1$, $b=2$, $b=3$. One will appear with the loop, one without, and one with a *cusp*. This last, the heart-shaped *Cardioid*, has many beautiful properties. It can be generated by a point on the rim of a circular disk rolling on another of equal size and also can be seen as the curve of light rays reflected from a polished cylinder.

5. *The Parabola*

Rene Descartes, the founder of modern Analytic Geometry, published the epoch-making treatise [**12**] "La Geometrie" in 1637. Contained in this monumental work is another attack upon the Trisection Problem, a solution by means of conic sections. The idea involved is that the roots of the Trisection Equation

$$x^3-3x-2a=0$$

can be represented as the x-coordinates of the points of intersection of a Parabola and a circle. Consider the Parabola:

$$y=x^2$$

and the circle: $$x^2+y^2-2hx-2ky=0,$$

whose center is at the point (h,k). The abscissas of their points of inter-

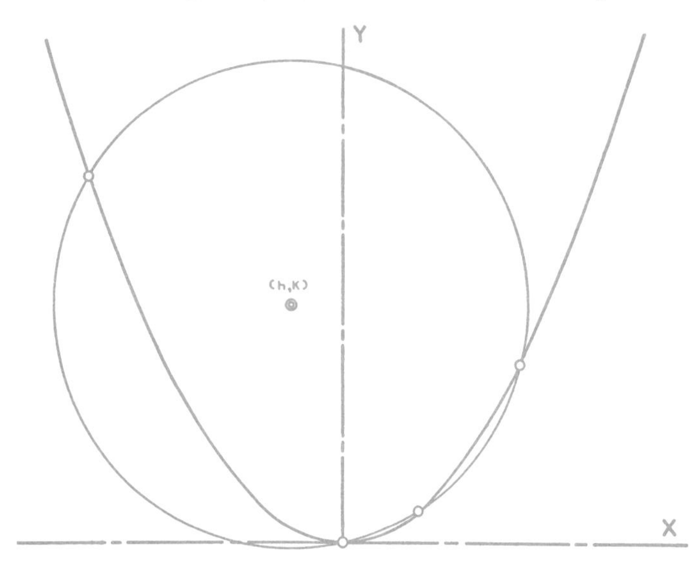

FIG. 9

section are found by eliminating y between their equations; thus, by substitution:

$$x^2+x^4-2hx-2kx^2=x[x^3-(2k-1)x-2h]=0.$$

The factor, $x=0$, which was expected since both curves pass through the origin, may be discarded. The other factor:

$$x^3-(2k-1)x-2h=0$$

can be the given Trisection Equation if we take particular values for h and k; that is, if

$$2k-1=3 \quad \text{or} \quad k=2 \quad \text{and} \quad h=a.$$

This is the requirement that the center of the circle be taken at $(a,2)$. With such arrangement, the circle will cut the Parabola in points whose abscissas are the roots of the Trisection Equation.

For illustration, let us apply this method to the trisection of 60°, the corresponding Equation for which is

$$x^3-3x-1=0.$$

Construct the Parabola $y=x^2$. Then draw the circle whose center is (1/2,2) and which passes through the origin O. The x-coordinate OC of a point of intersection is shown in Fig. 10.

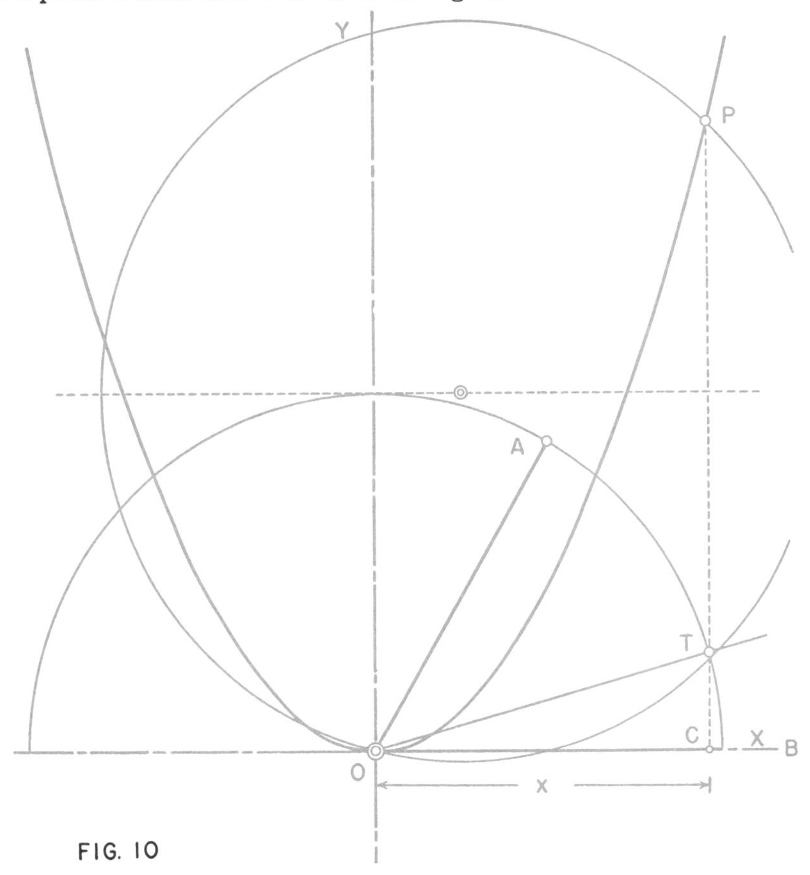

FIG. 10

It is obvious that the Parabola can be drawn once for all angles. When given any particular angle such as AOB (with OA selected as 2 units), drop the perpendicular from A to OB. Halve this projection and erect another perpendicular to meet the line $y=2$ at the center of the required circle. Draw the circle passing through the origin. From the point P, where this circle meets the Parabola, drop the perpendicular to OB. This will determine the root x of the Trisection Equation. But this value, see Fig. 1, is *twice* the projection value of the trisected part of AOB. That is, $x/2=\cos\Theta$. Thus we may either halve x and erect the perpendicular to meet the unit circle or, more conveniently, draw the circle with radius 2 meeting PC in T. The line OT then is a trisector of AOB.

Notice that the circle has for radius the quantity: $\sqrt{(2^2+a^2)}$. Thus, since the numerical value of a is never greater than 1, the largest radius of any circle needed is $\sqrt{5}$. For this reason, the Parabola need not be drawn beyond a certain range.

6. *The Cubic Parabola*

The curve whose equation is $y=x^3/2$ cuts the line

$$y=3x/2+a \tag{6.1}$$

in the points whose x-coordinates are given by the cubic equation:

$$x^3/2-3x/2+a=0 \qquad \text{or} \qquad x^3-3x-2a=0.$$

This system then may be used for trisection:

To each given angle with its projection value a there will correspond a certain line (6.1). All such lines have the same *slope:* 3/2;

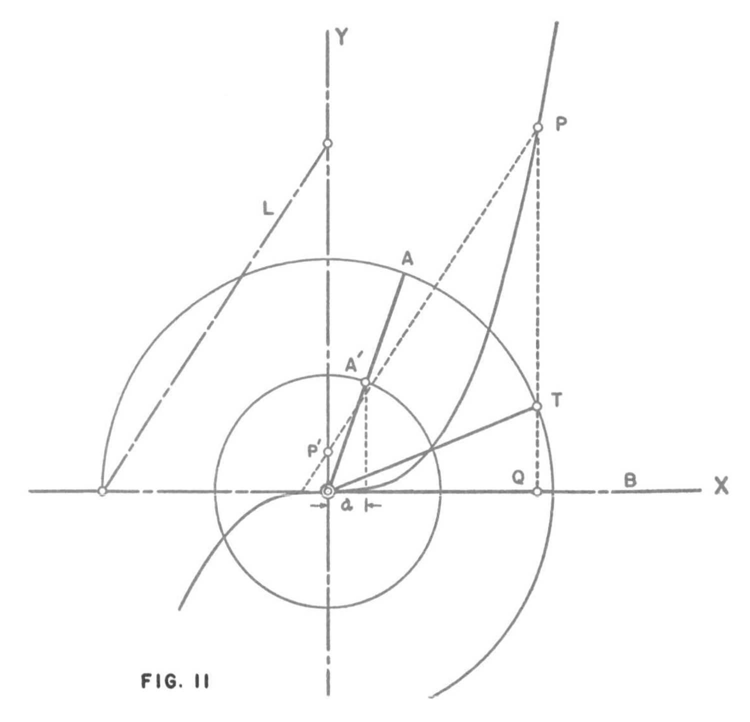

FIG. 11

that is, they are all parallel to the segment L drawn in Fig. 11. Furthermore, the line (6.1) corresponding to any given angle AOB cuts off upon the $Y-$axis a segment equal to a itself. The geometrical construction for the trisection of AOB is thus indicated: Draw the circles of radii 1 and 2 as shown. From A', where OA meets the unit circle, drop the perpendicular to find the projection a. Lay off this projection length $OP'=a$ upon the $Y-$axis and draw the line PP' parallel to L. From the intersection point P drop the perpendicular to OB, thus determining $OQ=x$, a root of the Trisection Equation. Now, as explained in the preceding paragraph, T is a point on the trisector.*

7. *The Cycloid of Ceva*

Prompted by the familiar "insertion" method (see Chapter III) of Archimedes, Ceva devised in 1699 a curve for trisection which was called the "Cycloidum anomalarum". The principle involved is that of doubling angles. With center C on the fixed line CB, draw the unit circle. A point P on a line rotating through C is located so that

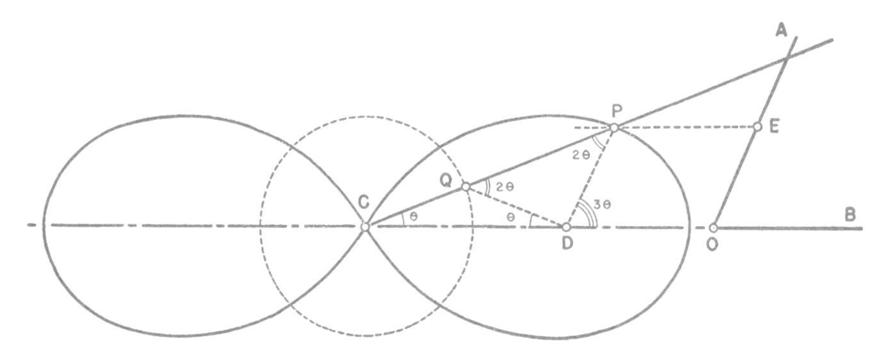

FIG. 12

$$CQ=QD=DP=1.$$

The locus of P, as AC revolves about C, is the curve in question. It is evident from the figure that if angle $QCD=\theta$, then

$$\angle QDC=\theta \quad \text{and} \quad \angle PQD=\angle QPD=\angle 2\theta.$$

Now since $\qquad \angle QDP=\pi-4\theta \quad \text{and} \quad \angle QDC=\theta,$

then $\qquad \angle PDO=3\theta \quad \text{and} \quad \angle QCD=\angle PDO/3.$

The application to a given angle AOB is as follows. Place one side, OB, of the angle coincident with the line CB. With the compasses lay off

*Points P in the first quadrant determine trisectors of given acute angles, while the other intersections in the third quadrant locate trisectors for the "induced" angles.

the unit length OE on OA. Then draw the line EP parallel to CB which strikes the curve at P. Then $\angle PCD = \angle AOB/3$.*

An equation of the curve in polar coordinates is:

$$\boxed{r = 1 + 2\cos 2\theta},$$

and in rectangular coordinates:

$$\boxed{(x^2+y^2)^3 = (3x^2-y^2)^2}.$$

The Cycloidum anomalarum is then a curve of the sixth degree. Compare the polar equation of this curve with that of the Limaçon.

8. *Remarks*

We found in Chapter I that the cubic Trisection Equation could not be solved by means of the first degree equation of a line and the second degree equation of the circle except when the Equation had constructible roots. In this chapter we have presented a number of solutions of the Trisection Equation in its general form, that is, for any value of a, but in each instance we made use of equations and corresponding curves which, excepting the conics, were of higher degree than the second.

Mathematical literature is crammed with such solutions of the Trisection Problem as are given in this chapter. It is an interesting fact that there exists an infinitude of curves, both transcendental and algebraic, which furnish the means of solving the problem. These curves, for the most part, are difficult to draw. Mechanical devices of various sorts have been invented for the description of these higher plane curves and, in many instances, these instruments may be used as trisectors in direct fashion. This is the subject of the following chapter.

*Lines EP cut the loop on both sides of its highest point. Those intersections to the right determine trisectors for acute angles while those to the left give trisectors for obtuse angles.

CHAPTER III

MECHANICAL TRISECTORS

A variety of mechanisms have been devised for the solution of the Trisection Problem. Some of these mechanisms draw the curves that aid in the solution of the Trisection Equation; others solve the equation directly or are applicable to the immediate division of the angle into three equal parts. It is with the latter sort that we shall concern ourselves in this chapter.

1. The Graduated Ruler

Undoubtedly known to Plato and Archimedes was the method of trisecting an angle by means of compasses and *graduated* ruler; that is, one along which marks have been spaced. These marks need not be any specified distance apart and, what is indeed surprising, there need be only *two* marks.

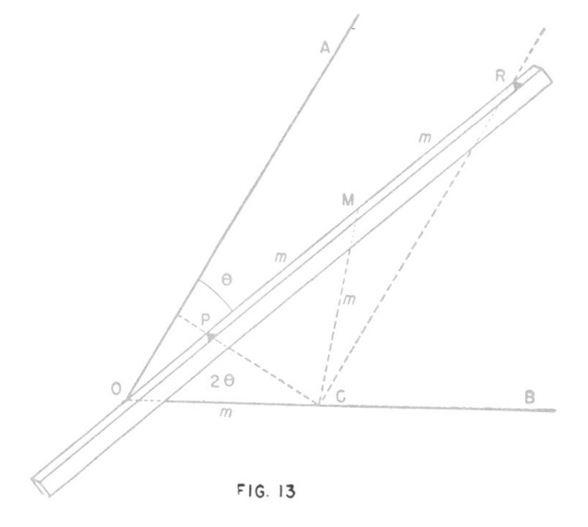

FIG. 13

(A) Let us suppose the ruler to have upon one edge* the two points P and R at a distance $2m$ apart. This distance is laid off on one side OB of the given angle. At the midpoint C of this segment,

*The other edge is not be used in constructions. A ruler with two straight edges is alone sufficient to make all constructions that are possible by the compasses and simple straightedge [51].

erect the lines perpendicular and parallel to OA. Then slide the ruler through O so that P and R become coincident with these constructed lines as shown in Fig. 13. In that position, the edge of the ruler trisects angle AOB. For, if M is the midpoint of PR,

$$PM = MR = MC = OC = m$$

so that, if $\angle AOR = \theta$, then $\angle MRC = \theta$, the alternate angle formed by the transversal OR and the parallels OA and CR. Since triangles CMR and OCM are isosceles,

$$\angle MCR = \theta, \quad \angle OMC = 2\theta = \angle COM$$

and OR is the trisecting line.

Let us look at the algebraic statement of this "sliding" process. Essentially, it is required that a given segment PR shall be so "inserted"

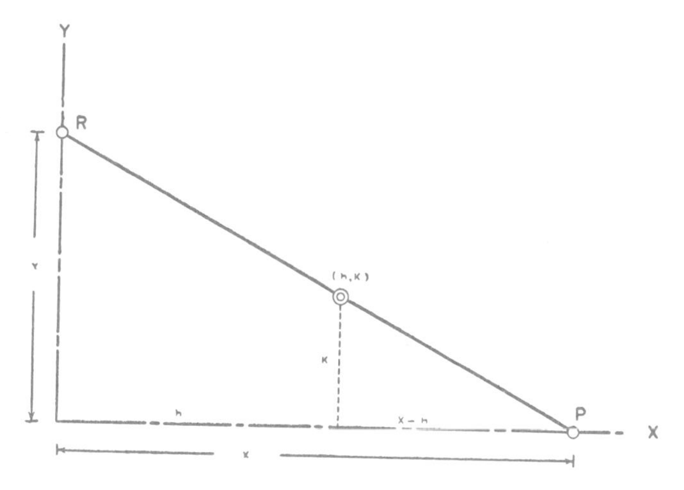

FIG. 14

between two fixed perpendicular lines that, extended if necessary, it shall pass through a fixed point O. Let the X and Y axes, Fig. 14, represent the perpendicular lines and let (h,k) be the coordinates of the fixed point. If x and y represent the intercepts of the segment PR, we must have:

$$x^2 + y^2 = 4m^2$$

for the constant length $PR = 2m$, and from similar triangles:

$$y/k = x/(x-h).$$

These two equations are now solved for x in terms of the given quantities h, k, and m. From the second $y = kx/(x-h)$ which, substituted in the first, gives:

$$x^2 + k^2x^2/(x-h)^2 = 4m^2,$$

or $$x^4 - 2hx^3 + (h^2 + k^2 - 4m^2)x^2 + 8hm^2x - 4h^2m^2 = 0.$$

Thus this insertion problem of Archimedes is one of the fourth degree; that is, there may be four possible positions of the segment. It is evident then that the possession of two marks upon the straightedge, although apparently innocent enough, forms a very powerful tool when used in the insertion manner.

It will be noticed that the insertion principle is fundamental to many of the devices explained in the following paragraphs.

(B) Another mode of solution by the graduated ruler follows directly from Fig. 1 of Chapter I. Construct at the vertex of the given angle AOB the circle with a radius equal to the distance between the marks on the ruler. That is,

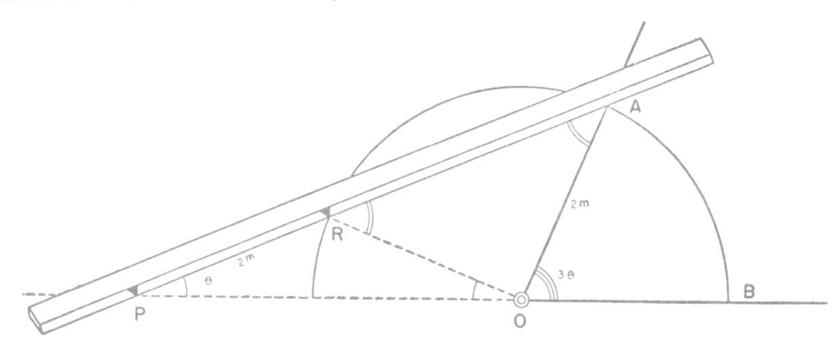

FIG 15

$$OR = OA = PR = 2m.$$

The points P and R of the ruler are brought into coincidence with the line OB (produced) and the circle, respectively, while the edge of the ruler slides through the point A. Since triangles PRO and ROA, Fig. 15, are isosceles,

$$\angle APO = \angle AOB/3.$$

2. *The Compasses of Hermes*

Exactly the same idea forms the basis of the compasses with three feet devised by H. Hermes in 1883 [**5**][**17**]. Here two points P and R, Fig. 16, attached to one leg of the compasses at a constant distance apart, are always in line with A, the point of the other leg. The circle with PR as radius is drawn about the vertex of the given angle. The

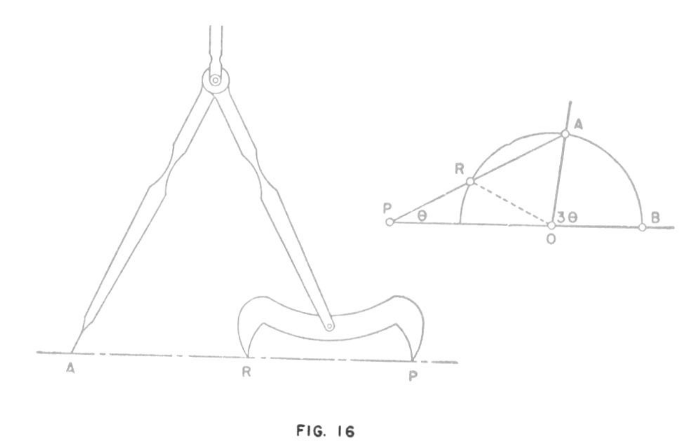

FIG. 16

point A of the compasses is applied to A on the side of the angle as shown and the compasses opened until P and R fall on the line OB and the circle, respectively. Then $\angle APB = \angle AOB/3$.

3. *A Three Bar Apparatus*

Under the insertion method falls the very simple arrangement of three bars shown in Fig. 17. Aubry [3] gives credit for this to Ceva but no doubt Pascal also used the instrument to draw his Limaçon.

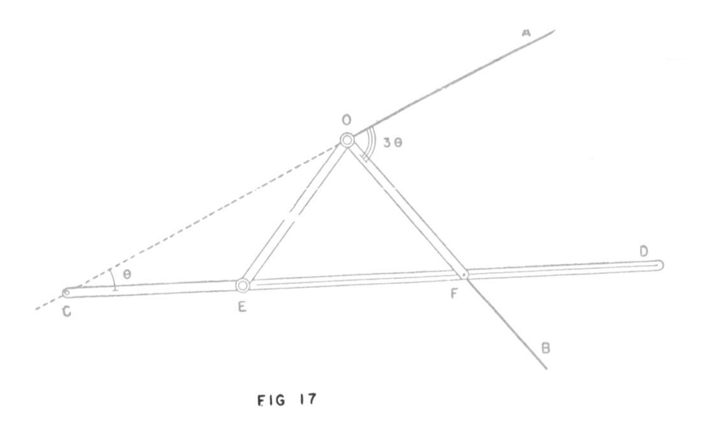

FIG 17

The bars OE and OF are taken equal in length and jointed together at O. The point E is attached so that $CE = OE$ and F is made to slide in a groove along CD. For trisection, the point O is placed at the vertex of the given angle AOB and OF coincident with OB. When C is brought to the produced line OA then

$$\angle ACD = \angle AOB/3.$$

It should be noticed that if CD is fixed, any point of OF traces out an Ellipse. To draw the Limacon, fix the bar OF and mark the path described by C. If the point C is fixed and O be made to move along a fixed straight line CA, then F describes the Cycloidum anomalarum of Ceva which was discussed in Chapter II.

4. *Ceva's Pantograph.*

Similar to the foregoing is the apparatus of Ceva, [**9**], which was considerably elaborated by Lagarrique in 1831 [**32**]. It is composed of four jointed bars forming a parallelogram with equal sides, two of which are extended. Its application to the angle AOB is shown in

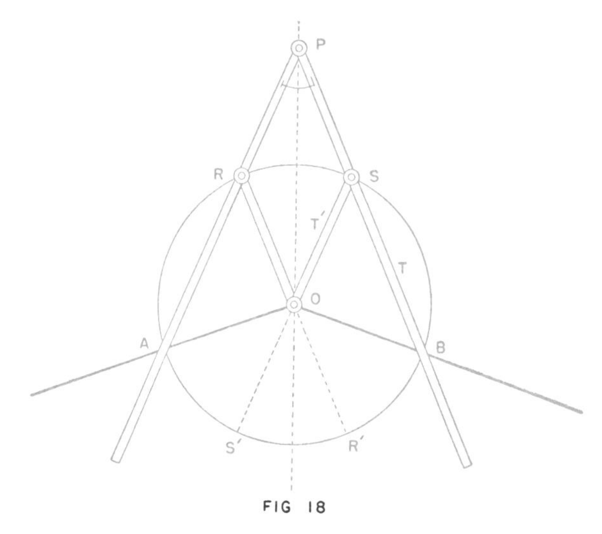

FIG 18

Fig. 18. The point O is placed at the vertex of AOB and P is made to move along the bisector of AOB until the extended sides of the parallelogram pass through A and B, the points where the circle of radius $OR = RP$ meets the sides of the given angle. Then, since arcs RS, AS', and BR', being subtended between parallel chords of the circle, are equal, $\angle ROS = \angle AOB/3$.

The instrument can be used as a Pantograph by fixing R to the plane and selecting a point T on SB as the tracer. Then the point T' on OS which is collinear with R and T describes a reduction of the path of T. Compare this device with the one shown in Fig. 17.

5. *Amadori's Instrument*

Again the same principle is involved in the apparatus of Amadori [**2**]. As indicated in Fig. 19, the straightedge is attached to a plate out of which are cut parts of the circle. The point P of the straightedge moves in a slot along the bisector of the given angle AOB while the other point R moves along the diameter of the circle, this diameter, of course, being equal to the distance PR. When the

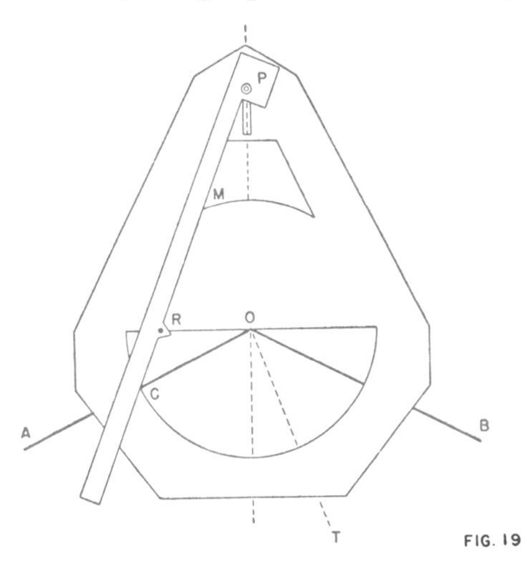

FIG. 19

edge passes through C then the point M determines the trisecting line MOT.

The mechanisms of the preceding paragraphs all contained as the fundamental principle the ability to insert a given segment either between two lines or between a line and a circle in such a way that the line upon which the segment lies passes through some fixed point. The following two very novel and ingenious devices employ the insertion idea but with the different requirement that a line fixed at right angles to the segment shall pass through a given fixed point.

6. *The Carpenter's Square*

A right-angled square with parallel eges whose legs have the same width m, Fig. 20, is first used to draw the line $O'B'$ parallel to OB. It is then placed so that its inner edge passes through O with the corners P and R on OA and $O'B'$ respectively so that $PR = 2m$. In this position, it is readily seen that the right triangles, OPT, ORT, and ORK are all congruent with equal angles at O. Then OT and OR are trisecting lines of angle AOB [**44**]. The square was used by

Nicholson, [**37**], to draw a trisecting curve and a little later by Aubry [**3**] in this more direct fashion [**51**].

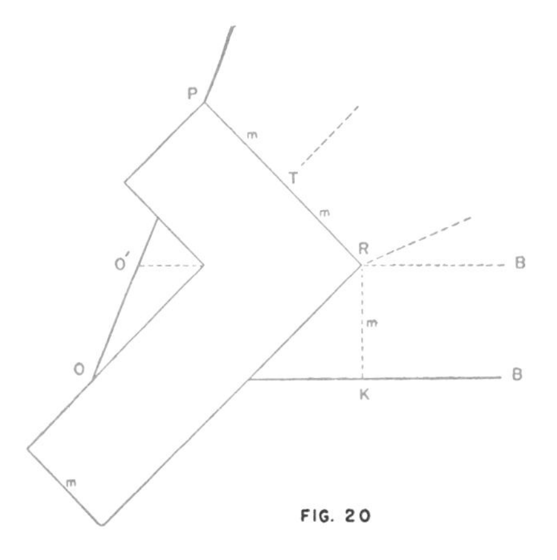

FIG. 20

7. The Tomahawk

This implement is, in a sense, an improvement over the carpenter's square since it is directly applicable to the trisection of a given angle. Furthermore, the edges of the "handle" need not be parallel to each

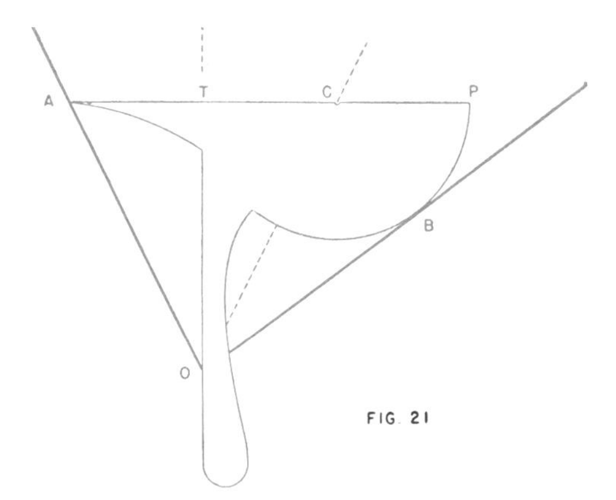

FIG. 21

other. TBP is a semicircle, Fig. 21, with OT a tangent. The point C is the center of the semicircle and A is taken on PT extended so that AT is equal to the radius of the circle. As in Paragraph 6, OT and OC are trisecting lines.

Although the inventor of the Tomahawk is not known, Bergery describes the instrument in the 3rd edition of *Geométrie appliquée a l'industrie,* Metz, 1835. See also [**22**].

8. *Laisant's Compasses*

A mechanism composed of four straight bars hinged together at one point and forced to make equal angles with each other was given by Laisant [**33**] in 1875. The lengths are chosen so that, Fig. 22,

$$OB = OC, \quad CS' = BS', \quad OD = OA, \quad AS = DS,$$

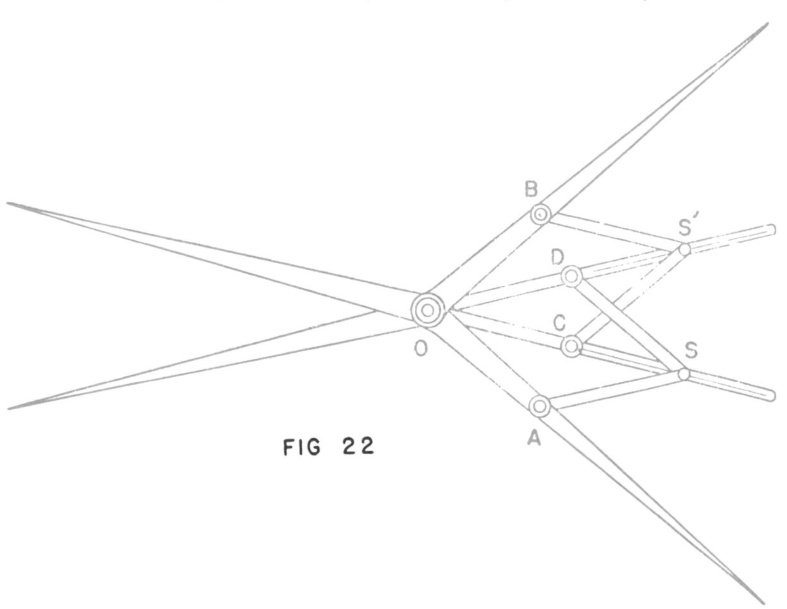

FIG 22

with S and S' as joints permitted to slide in straight grooves along the two trisecting bars. The triangles OBS', ODS', and OAS are congruent with equal angles at O. The bars OS' and OS are extended beyond O so that the third part can be set off upon the same arc.

9. *Laisant's Mechanism*

Somewhat different is a second device offered by Laisant, ibid. See also [**7**]. $OBCD$ and $CDES$, Fig. 23, are jointed parallelograms with all sides equal. The joint S is forced to move in a straight groove along the rod OD extended. Triangles CBO and CDO are congruent with equal angles at O. Moreover, the same is true of triangles SCO and SEO. Thus

$$\angle BOC = \angle COS = \angle SOE = \angle AOB/3.$$

A glance at the three bars $ODES$ will indicate the connection between this instrument and that shown in Fig. 17, Paragraph 3. Notice that if the bar OB is held fixed, the point E will describe a Limaçon.

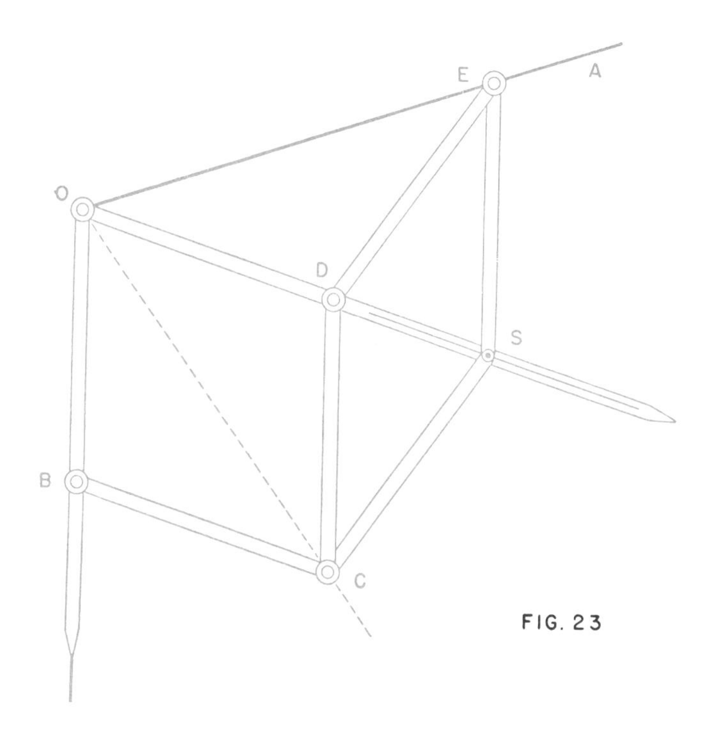

FIG. 23

10. Kempe's Trisector

One of the cleverest amateur mathematicians of the past century was A. B. Kempe who, in 1875, was a young London barrister specializing in ecclesiastical law. To him is due the following elegant mechanism for direct trisection [**29**].

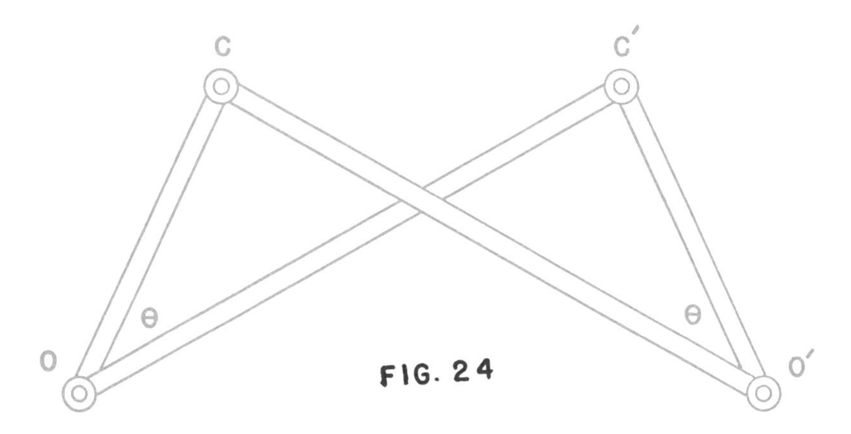

FIG. 24

Consider the jointed *crossed parallelogram* $OC'O'C$, Fig. 24, composed of four bars equal in pairs. That is,

$$OC = O'C' = b \quad \text{and} \quad OC' = O'C = c.$$

It is evident that no matter how the mechanism is deformed,

$$\angle COC' = \angle CO'C' = \theta.$$

Now let us attach two more bars OD and DE as shown in Fig. 25 so that

$$DE = OC = b \quad \text{and} \quad OD = CE = d.$$

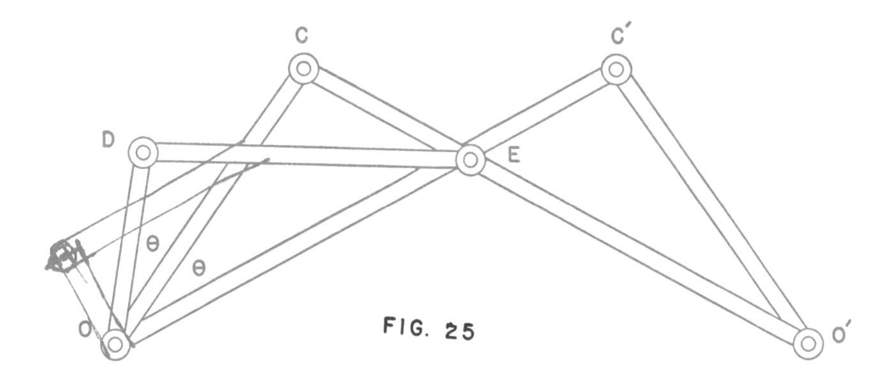

FIG. 25

With this, $ODEC$ itself is another smaller crossed parallelogram with

$$\angle DOC = \angle CED.$$

Let us see if it is possible to arrange matters so that $\angle DOC = \angle COC' = \theta$ throughout all deformations of the second mechanism. If these angles are to be equal, the two crossed parallelograms are always similar since they already have equal angles at D, C, and C'. Consequently, we must have the proportion:

$$OD/OC = OC/OC' \quad \text{or} \quad d/b = b/c,$$

or

$$b^2 = cd.$$

This means that the length of OC (and of $O'C'$) must be a mean proportional between the lengths OC' and OD; for example, $d = 1$, $b = 2$, $c = 4$.

From this discussion, it is obvious that two more bars, OF and FG, may be attached in the same fashion to give *three* equal angles at O, thus producing the Kempe trisector shown in Fig. 26. For the construction of the mechanism, it will be found convenient to take 1, 2, 4, and 16 inches as appropriate lengths.

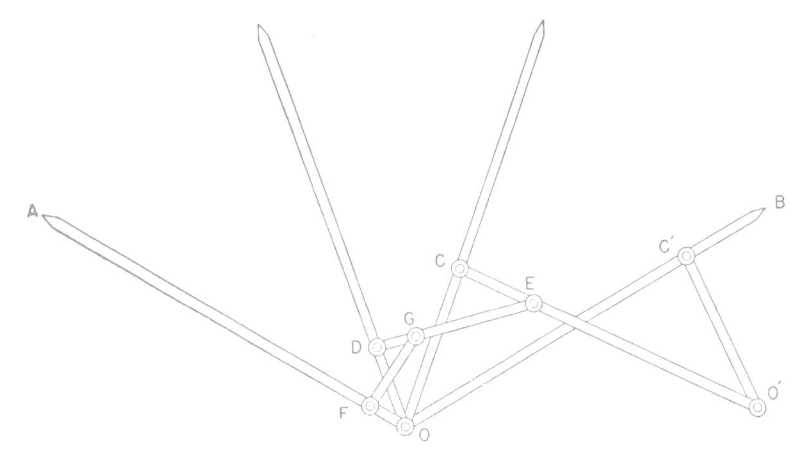

FIG 26

11. A Linkage

With the Kempe arrangement of two crossed parallelograms, we may now improve on the Laisant mechanism of Paragraph 9 [**51**]. Returning to Fig. 23, it will be noticed that the purpose of the slide S is to keep the bars CD and ED equally inclined to OD. Accordingly,

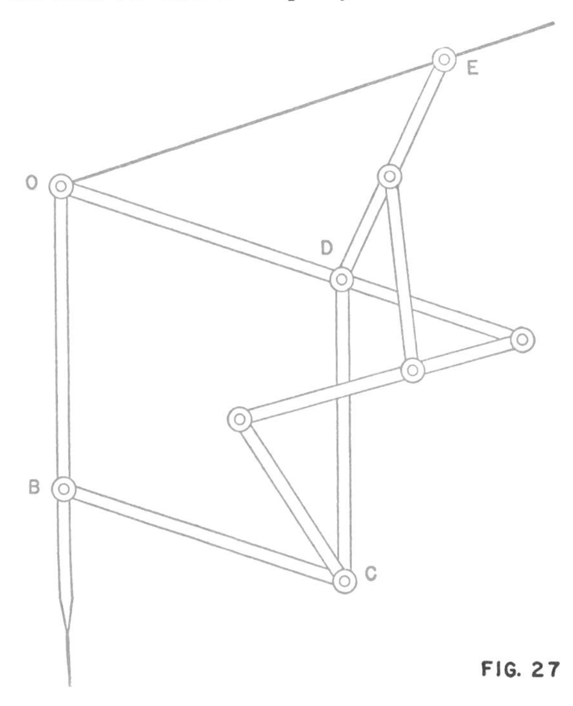

FIG. 27

by properly attaching crossed parallelograms to these three bars, this equal inclination may be accomplished and the useless bars CS and ES removed without otherwise altering the effect of the mechanism. We have then, Fig. 27, a linkage free from the slide and groove combination that is mechanically undesirable.

12. *Sylvester's Isoklinostat*

Another linkage trisector was announced by Sylvester [**47**] in 1875 under the title "A Lady's Fan". The joints A, B, C, D, E, F, G lie on a circle with center at O so that $AH=HB$ and $BK=KC$, etc. Thus $\angle AOB=\angle COD=\angle EOF$ and $\angle BOC=\angle DOE=\angle FOG$. Accordingly,

$$\angle AOC=\angle COE=\angle EOG.$$

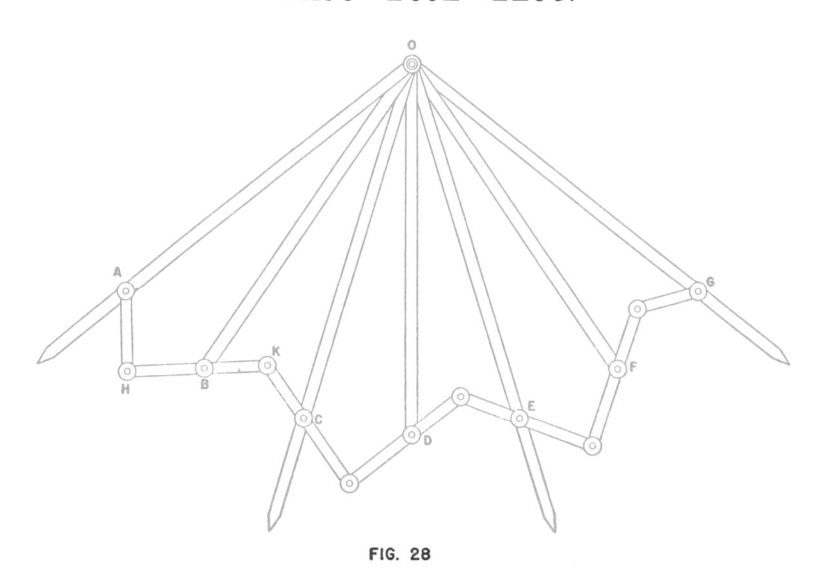

FIG. 28

Shortly after its appearance this mechanism was utilized in an optical apparatus to keep moving prisms equally inclined to each other.

13. *A Line Motion Trisector*

Consider the figures of Paragraphs 9 and 11. In Fig. 23, the point S was constrained to move along the diagonal of the rhombus $CDES$. Let us put the bars ES and CS back into place in Fig. 27. It is clear then that S would move always in line with bar OD. Consequently, *if the bar OD were held fixed as shown in Fig. 29, then S would move in the straight line determined by this bar* [**29**].

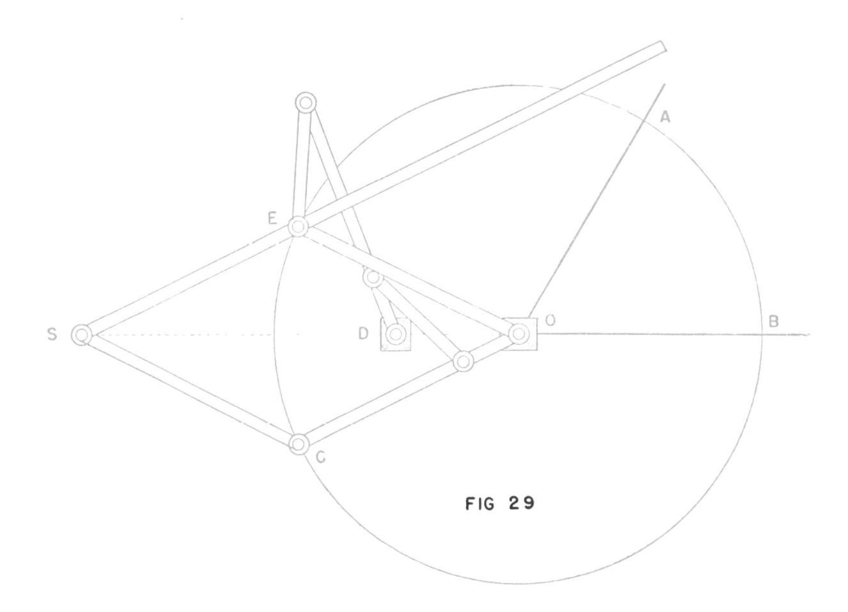

FIG 29

Let the side of the rhombus $OCSE$ be the unit length. By fixing the diagonal OD in a horizontal position, E will move on the unit circle about O, and S along its horizontal diameter. This, it will be noticed, is precisely the underlying principle of the insertion method explained in Paragraph 1. Thus if the bar SE be extended as shown here we need only move this bar so that it will pass through A in order to trisect angle AOB. The angle OSE will, of course, be $\angle AOB/3$.

14. *Draughting Triangles*

Two celluloid triangles, each having a right angle, are sufficient equipment to trisect any angle [**1**] [**17**]. Let $AOB = 3\theta$ be the given angle about which is drawn the unit circle, Fig. 30. As usual, a will denote the projection of one unit side upon the other, that is, $a = \cos 3\theta$. Draw the two perpendicular diameters of the circle and mark off two units on the vertical one below the circle to P. At P lay off the distance $2a$ horizontally to S. Slide the two triangles along with their two edges together until the other perpendicular edges pass through S and T. At the same time, the corresponding right angle vertices should lie on the vertical and horizontal lines, respectively. In this position, the line AC determines the angle $\theta = \angle AOB/3$. Let x represent the distance CO and z the distance MP. Since CD and LM are parallel, they make equal angles with the horizontal and thus

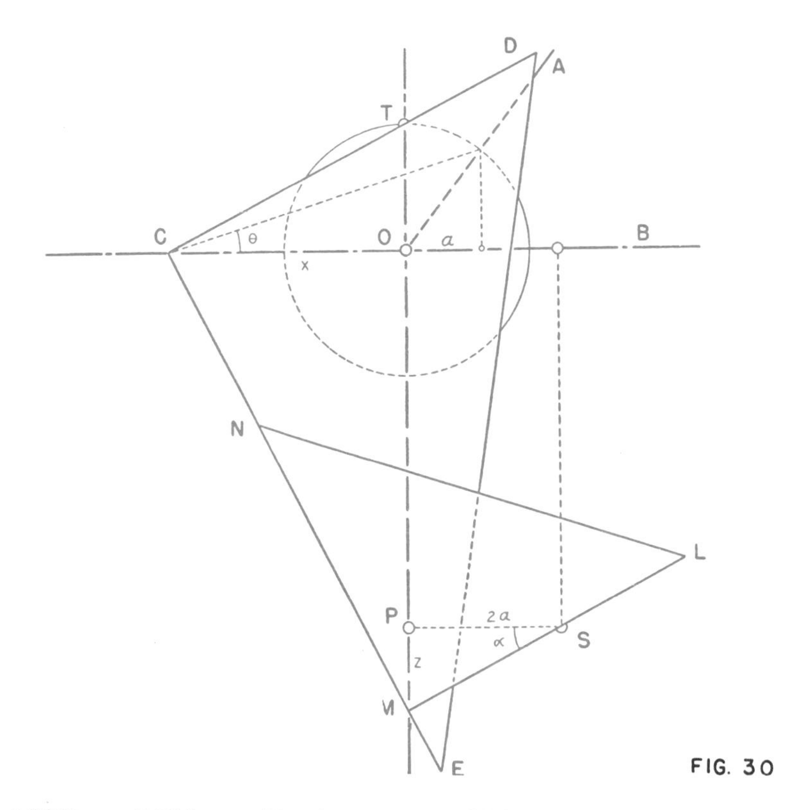

FIG. 30

$\angle OCT = \angle PSM = \alpha$. Furthermore, $\angle CMO = \alpha$. Therefore, the right triangles COT, MOC, and SPM are similar and we have the proportion:

$$1/x = x/(3+z) = z/2a.$$

From the first and last members here: $z = 2a/x$ which, substituted in the first two members, gives:

$$1/x = x^2/(3x+2a),$$

or

$$x^3 - 3x - 2a = 0,$$

the Trisection Equation.

15. *The Cone Trisector*

The following trisection, given by Aubry [**3**] is included here for its novelty. A right circular cone, Fig. 31, is constructed having its slant height equal to three times the base radius. The cone is placed so that the center of the base is coincident with the vertex of the given

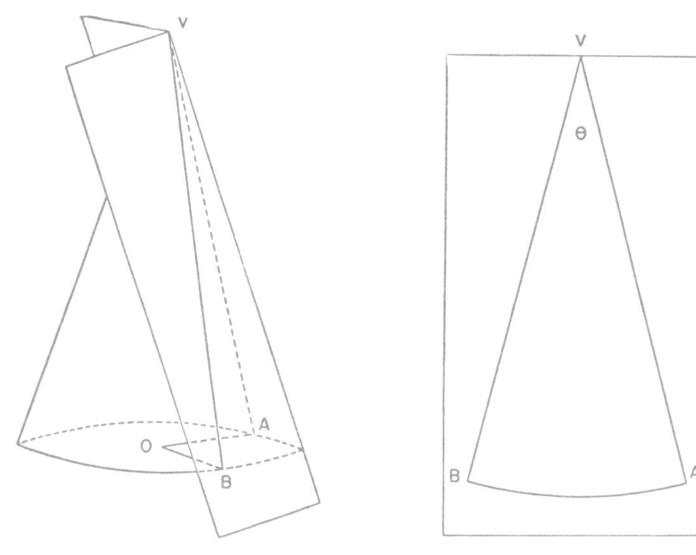

FIG 31

angle, $AOB = 3\theta$. Then arc $AB = 3r\theta$. A sheet of paper is now wrapped around the cone and the points A, B, and V are marked on it as shown. When the sheet is removed and flattened out, the angle AVB is one-third angle AOB. For, since $AV = 3r$,

$$\text{arc } AB = 3r(\angle AVB),$$

and thus

$$\angle AVB = \theta = \angle AOB/3.$$

16. Remarks

It has been said that Plato objected to all constructions which involved the use of any mathematical instrument other than the straigthedge and compasses. Yet there is every indication that he himself proposed for the solution of the cubic a mechanical arrangement very similar to the pair of right triangles of Paragraph 14. Some historians credit him with the following statement concerning the practice of mechanical solutions: "The good of geometry is set aside and destroyed, for we again reduce it to the world of sense, instead of elevating and imbuing it with the eternal and incorporeal images of thought, even as it is employed by God, for which reason He always is God." Of course, it is and was realized that the actual drawings made by these instruments were but crude physical representations of the ideals in mind—the "eternal and incorporeal images of thought." But there is nothing un-mathematical about the use of a graduated ruler or any other instrument capable of making appropriate illustrations and physical applications of theory.

By adopting tools other than the classical ones and by altering Platonian rules many interesting and important contributions have been made to the whole field of mathematics. Mascheroni, for example, performed an amazing feat when he proved that the whole of the plane geometry of Euclid could be reconstructed by throwing the straightedge into discard and using only the compasses. If such a possibility had occurred to the Ancients they certainly would not have labeled the straightedge as an instrument of the gods. It too would have been banned and shunned as a degraded tool fit only for the baser uses of the mechanic.

CHAPTER IV

APPROXIMATIONS

Sufficient for any purpose are a large number of constructions by straightedge and compasses which, although simple, give remarkably good approximations [**49**] for trisecting a given angle. Many of these are of long standing and exhibit considerable ingenuity of construction. Individuals who think they have found exact methods of trisection of the general angle by straightedge and compasses have actually found nothing more than approximations. Of course, a large number of these attempts yield very accurate results and to the eye the drawings appear successsful indeed. Dependence on such a physical impression, however, often brings about unfortunate conclusions.

1. An Unending Construction

Fialkowski [**19**] in 1860, based an approximation upon the series:

$$S_n = 1/2 - 1/2^2 + 1/2^3 - 1/2^4 + \cdots \pm 1/2^n. \tag{1.1}$$

If this series is multiplied through by (1/2), it becomes:

$$S_n/2 = 1/2^2 - 1/2^3 + 1/2^4 - 1/2^5 + \cdots \pm 1/2^{n+1}.$$

Now, by adding the two equations, we have the compact expression for the sum:

$$3S_n/2 = 1/2 \pm 1/2^{n+1},$$

or

$$S_n = (1/3)(1 \pm 1/2^n).$$

As n is allowed to grow larger, it is evident that the value of S_n grows nearer equal to 1/3. Thus, for example, on taking eight terms of the series, $n=8$, S_n differs from 1/3 by an amount equal to $1/2^8$; taking $n=9$, S_n differs from 1/3 by $1/2^9$; etc.

For the application of this to the approximate trisection of $AOB = \Phi$, let S_n represent the ratio Θ_n/Φ, where Θ_n is the angle to be constructed at the nth step. That is,

$$\Theta_n = (1/3)(1 \pm 1/2^n) \cdot \Phi. \tag{1.2}$$

It is apparent from this that the larger we take n, the nearer will Θ_n equal $\Phi/3$, or $AOB/3$. Let us agree that a positive angle is to be measured from OB towards OA, a negative angle in the opposite

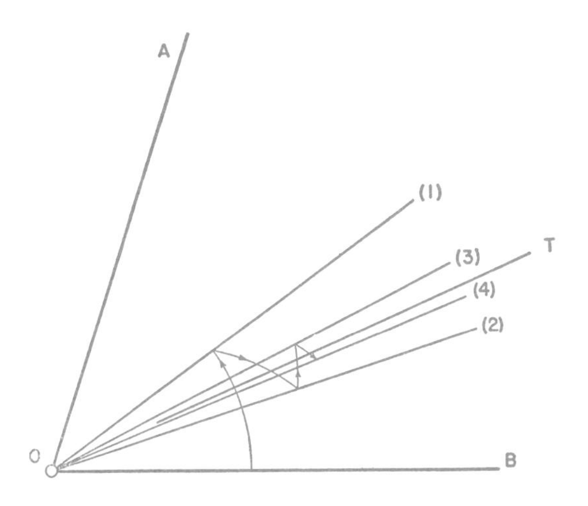

FIG. 32

direction. The steps in the construction are indicated in (1.2): first, bisect angle AOB, obtaining the line (1); then bisect angle $BO(1)$, obtaining the line (2); etc., alternately adding and subtracting as shown. The process leads step by step toward the actual position of the trisecting line OT. It must be realized, however, that no matter how large n be chosen, Θ_n will differ by *some* amount from $\Phi/3$. For example, if eight steps be taken for the angle $AOB = \Phi = 60°$, equation (1.2) gives:

$$\Theta_8 = (60°/3)(1 - 2^8) = 20° - 20°/2^8,$$

so that Θ_8 is too small by less than five minutes.

2. *Approximation of von Cusa and Snellius*

Consider the sector AOB of the unit circle with the segments AC and BD drawn perpendicular to OB. If the central angle be measured in radians, then

$$AC = \sin\Theta, \quad \text{arc } AB = \Theta, \quad BD = \tan\Theta.$$

Evidently these lengths satisfy the inequality:

$$\sin\Theta \leq \Theta \leq \tan\Theta. \tag{2.1}$$

Nikolaus von Cusa, who lived in the 15th century, noticed that the quantity:

$$(1+n)\sin\theta/(n+\cos\theta) \tag{2.2}$$

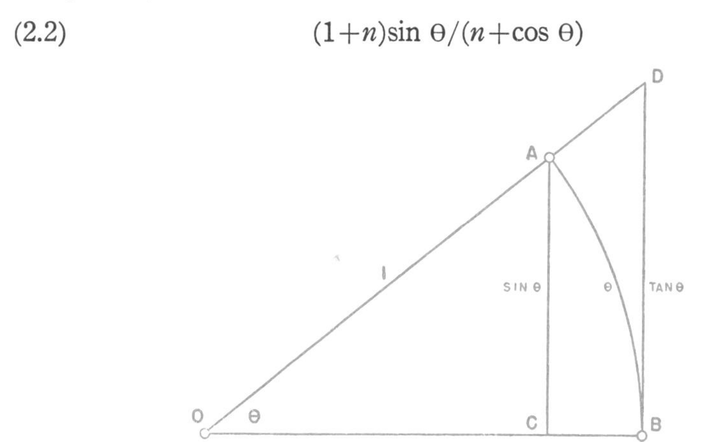

FIG. 33

is, for $n=0$, equal to $\tan\theta$ and thus, by (2.1), *greater* than θ; moreover, as n approaches infinity the ratio approaches $\sin\theta$, a quantity *less* than θ. He accordingly proposed the following question: For what value of n is this quantity the best approximation for θ? The answer he gave is $n=2$. Let us see for ourselves.

If the quantity (2.2) is to be a good approximation for θ then we should be able to make the difference between the quantity and the exact value of θ as small as we please. This difference is:

$$\begin{aligned} D &= [(1+n)\sin\theta/(n+\cos\theta)]-\theta \\ &= [(1+n)\sin\theta - n\theta - \theta\cos\theta]/(n+\cos\theta). \end{aligned}$$

By using well known expressions for $\sin\theta$ and $\cos\theta$ directly in terms of θ this difference can be written in the form:

$$D=\frac{[(1+n)(\theta-\theta^3/3!+\theta^5/5!-\cdots)-n\theta-\theta(1-\theta^2/2!+\theta^4/4!-\cdots)]}{(n+\cos\theta)}$$

or $D=(2-n)\theta^3/6(n+\cos\theta)+(n-4)\theta^5/120(n+\cos\theta)+(\ \ )\theta^7+\cdots$.

If θ, measured in radians, is numerically less than 1, the terms in the right member diminish rapidly as the series is extended.

It may be seen that the result, $n=2$, arrived at empirically by von Cusa, is in fact the best possible choice for $|\theta|<1$. For, by putting $n=2$ in this last equation, the first power of θ to appear is the 5th and the whole right hand member is considerably less than if the 3rd power were present. Willebrod Snellius, in the next century, was the first to consider the von Cusa question on a rigorous basis and equal credit for the method should belong to him.*

We may thus establish the approximation formula:

$$\theta=3 \sin \theta/(2+\cos \theta).$$

In order to see the geometrical meaning contained in the formula,

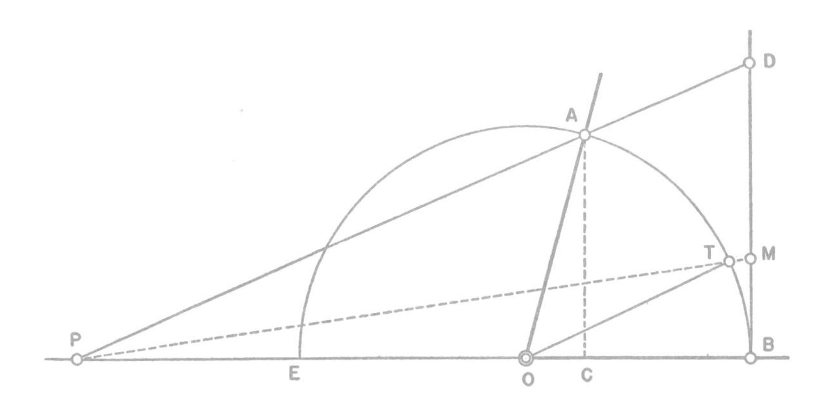

FIG. 34

extend the diameter BE of the unit circle, Fig. 34, to P, so that $EP=1$. The line PA strikes the tangent at D. From the similar triangles PCA and PBD, we have the proportion:

$$AC/PC=BD/PB,$$

or, since $AC=\sin \theta$, $PC=2+\cos \theta$, $PB=3$:

$$BD=3 \sin \theta/(2+\cos \theta).$$

Thus the approximation made by von Cusa is that of replacing the arc length subtending angle AOB by the tangent length BD.

For the approximate trisection of angle AOB we need only locate the point M so that $BM=BD/3$ and join it to P. The line PM will cut the unit circle in T. The line joining T to O thus approximately trisects angle AOB. A table of errors for angles from 0° to 90° follows:

*Snellius in his *Cyclometria* figured π by using polygons up to 5,242,880 sides.

Angle	*Error*	*Angle*	*Error*	*Angle*	*Error*
10°	13″	40°	15′ 4″	70°	1°28′
20°	1′51″	50°	30′ 6″	80°	2°17′
30°	6′20″	60°	53′20″	90°	3°27′

3. *Dürer's Approximation*

Extremely elegant in both its simplicity and accuracy is the early approximation of Albrech Dürer which appeared [**15**] in 1525. Let the chord and the subtended arc of the unit circle be constructed upon the given angle $AOB = 2\Theta$. The points M_1, M_2 are located dividing

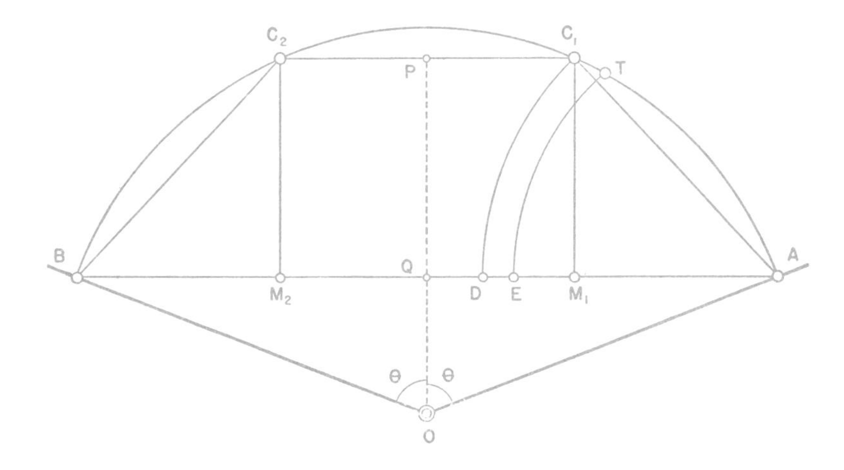

FIG. 35

the chord into three equal parts and at these points perpendiculars are erected to meet the arc in C_1 and C_2. It was Dürer's plan to construct the average between the chord lengths, AC_1, C_1C_2, and C_2B in as few steps as possible. To this end, he described the arc C_1D with A as center and AC_1 as radius. Then, locating the point E such that $EM_1 = 2(DE)$, a second arc, center at A and radius AE, was drawn intersecting the circle at T. The line OT then was his approximate trisecting line.

In order to show the degree of accuracy of this construction, draw the bisecting line OP so that PC_1 is parallel to the chord AB. The following relations are determined with the help of the figure:

$$OQ = \cos\Theta; \quad AQ = \sin\Theta; \quad AB = 2\sin\Theta; \quad AM_1 = (2\sin\Theta)/3;$$

$$PC_1 = AQ - AM_1 = (\sin\theta)/3; \quad OP = \sqrt{(OC_1^2 - PC_1^2)} = (1/3)\sqrt{(9 - \sin^2\theta)};$$

$$PQ = C_1M_1 = OP - OQ = (1/3)\sqrt{(9-\sin^2\theta)} - \cos\theta;$$

$$AC_1 = AD = \sqrt{(AM_1^2 + C_1M_1^2)} = \sqrt{(2/3)}\sqrt{2+\cos^2\theta - \cos\theta\sqrt{8+\cos^2\theta}}.$$

Now by construction:

$$\begin{aligned} AT = AE = AM_1 + M_1E &= AM_1 + (2/3)(M_1D) \\ &= AM_1 + (2/3)(AD - AM_1) = (1/3)(AM_1 + 2\cdot AD), \end{aligned}$$

which is precisely the average of the chords AC_1, C_1C_2, C_2B, which Dürer planned. We have for this, on substituting the expressions for AM_1 and AD in terms of θ:

$$AT = (2/9)\sin\theta + (2\sqrt{2}/3\sqrt{3})\cdot\sqrt{2+\cos^2\theta - \cos\theta\cdot\sqrt{8+\cos^2\theta}},$$

the length of the approximate trisecting chord in terms of the given angle. Thus, since

$$2\sin(AOT/2) = AT \quad \text{or} \quad AOT = 2\cdot \text{arc}\sin(AT/2),$$

we have:

$$\angle AOT = 2\cdot\text{arc}\sin\left[(1/9)\sin\theta + \sqrt{(2/27)}\cdot\sqrt{2+\cos^2\theta - \cos\theta\cdot\sqrt{8+\cos^2\theta}}\right]$$

as the approximate third part of the given angle. A table of errors for angles between 0° and 180° gives an indication of the remarkable accuracy:

Angle	*Error*	*Angle*	*Error*
60°	1″	140°	5′37″
90°	18″	140°	9′ 4″
120°	1′56″	180°	31′38″

Before passing on, we must recall to the reader's mind a few of the accomplishments of this remarkable man. He is perhaps best known for his etchings and paintings. A champion of the art of perspective, he organized the information developed up to his time into the first text book on the subject. His etching, *Melancholia*, is to be found in many present day books on architecture and mathematics.

4. *Karajordanoff's Approximation*

Dropping down several centuries to recent times, we find a simple approximation discovered by Karajordanoff in 1928 [**5**]. The circles of radii 1 and 2 are drawn about the angle AOB. The tangent to the unit circle at A meets the chord BC in D, where C is the midpoint of AB. The line through D parallel to OB intersects the larger circle in T and OT is the approximate trisecting line.

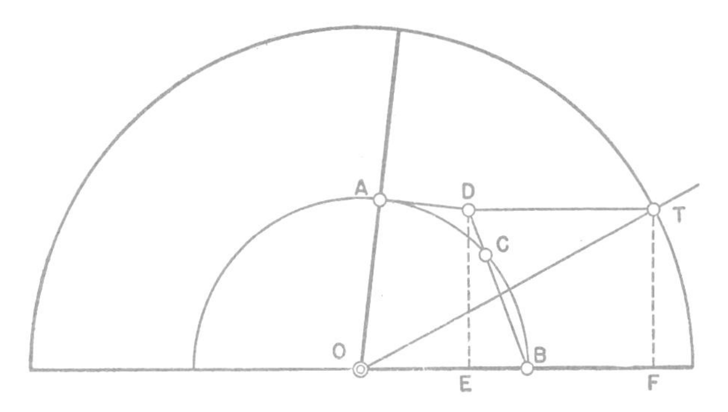

FIG. 36

We seek the error committed in trisecting various angles by this method. Making use of rectangular coordinates with O for origin and OB as X-axis, the coordinates of the several points are:

$$A : (\cos 2\theta, \sin 2\theta); \quad B : (1,0); \quad C : (\cos \theta, \sin \theta),$$

where $\angle AOB = 2\theta$.

The line through B and C has for its equation:

$$x = 1 - y \cdot \tan(\theta/2)$$

while the tangent to the smaller circle at A is (with negative reciprocal slope of OA):

$$x \cos 2\theta + y \sin 2\theta = 1.$$

The two lines meet at D, the y-coordinate, DE, of which is obtained by eliminating x between the two:

$$y = (1 - \cos 2\theta)/[\sin 2\theta - \cos 2\theta \ \tan(\theta/2)].$$

This, by construction, is the length of the segment FT and, since $OT = 2$:

$$\angle FOT = \text{arc} \sin[(1 - \cos 2\theta)\sin\theta/2(\cos\theta - \cos 2\theta)].$$

Errors for angles between 0° and 90° follow:

Angle	*Error*	*Angle*	*Error*	*Angle*	*Error*
10°	1″	40°	45″	70°	2′12″
20°	6″	50°	1′19″	80°	1′50″
30°	21″	60°	1′53″	90°	0

Although this method of Karajordanoff is not as accurate as Dürer's for some angles, it has a redeeming feature: the error does not always increase as the given angles increase to 90°. A maximum error occurs at 70°15′ with a value less than two and one-third minutes.

5. *Kopf-Perron Approximation*

A comparative study of the arc lengths of a particular circle and the trisecting Limaçon of Pascal led Kopf in 1919 to the following method, which was refined somewhat later by Perron [**40**] and d'Ocagne [**38**].

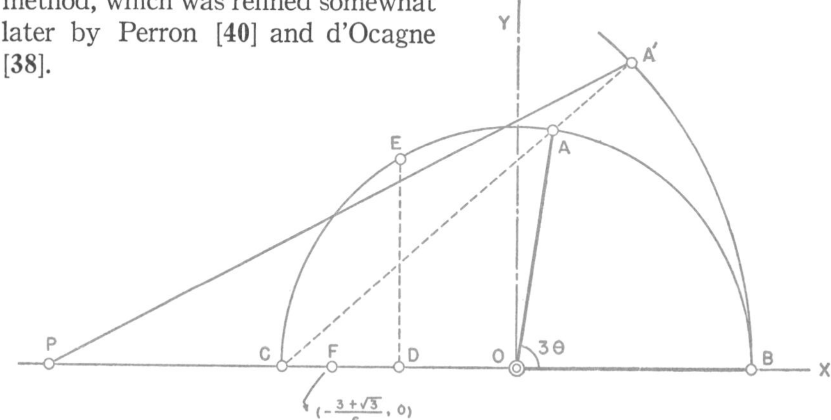

FIG. 37

The unit circle cuts the sides of the given angle at A and B. The midpoint D of OC is marked, PC is taken equal to 1, and DF as one-third the length DE; that is, since $OD=1/2$, $OE=1$:

$$DE=\sqrt{3}/2 \quad \text{and} \quad DF=\sqrt{3}/6.$$

With center at F: $$\left(-\frac{3+\sqrt{3}}{6}, 0\right)$$

and radius $FB=1+(3+\sqrt{3})/6$, the arc BA' is constructed. The line CA meets this arc in A' and angle $A'PB$ is approximately $\angle AOB/3$. The errors committed for various angles have already been tabulated by Perron:

Angle	*Error*	*Angle*	*Error*	*Angle*	*Error*
12°	0.18″	48°	8.58″	84°	8.47″
24°	1.38″	60°	13.08″	90°	0
36°	4.23″	72°	14.76″		

The error, as in the method of Karajordanoff, is not an increasing one. The maximum of 14.9″ occurs at 69°57′40″.

6. *Approximation of D'Ocagne*

A recent and extremely simple method that is surprisingly accurate for small angles is given by d'Ocagne [**38**]. From the midpoint C of the radius of the unit circle, the line CM is drawn to the midpoint of the arc of the given angle AOB. Then angle MCB is approximately one-third angle AOB.

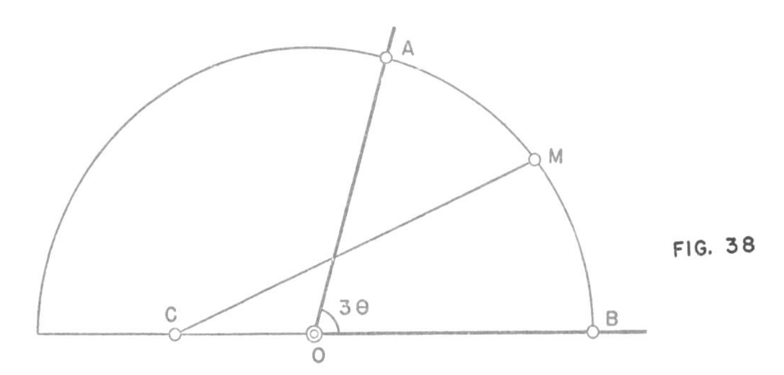

FIG. 38

The coordinates of M are $\left(\cos\frac{3\theta}{2}, \sin\frac{3\theta}{2}\right)$.

Thus: $$\angle MCB = \arctan\left[2\cdot\sin\frac{3\theta}{2}\Big/\left(1+2\cos\frac{3\theta}{2}\right)\right].$$

The errors are:

Angle	*Error*	*Angle*	*Error*	*Angle*	*Error*
10°	1.5″	40°	1′48″	70°	10′
20°	2.64″	50°	3′26″	80°	15′
30°	45″	60°	6′14″	90°	21′41″

7. *Comparison of Methods*

The following chart affords a comparison of the methods of approximation given in this chapter. Errors are plotted against corresponding angles.

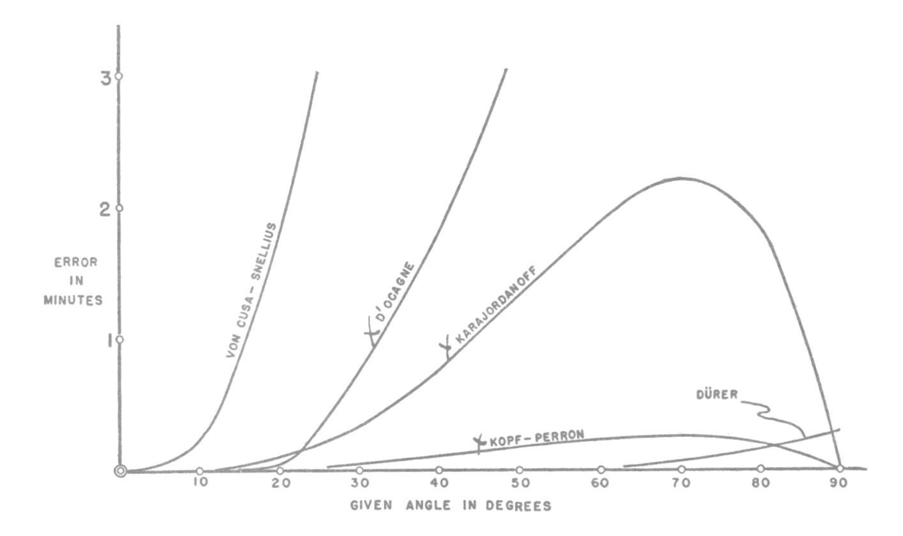
3
2
1
ERROR
IN
MINUTES
VON CUSA - SNELLIUS
D'OCAGNE
KARAJORDANOFF
DÜRER
KOPF - PERRON
10
20
30
40
50
60
70
80
90
GIVEN ANGLE IN DEGREES

FIG. 39

CHAPTER V

DON QUIXOTES

P. L. Wantzel in 1837 (see Liouville's Journal, II, p. 366) was the first to give a rigorous proof of the impossibility of trisecting the general angle by straightedge and compasses. (Gauss had already made the statement in his Disquisitiones Arithmeticæ but neglected to give the proof). He was able to do this, however, only after far-reaching discoveries had been made in the fields of algebraic analysis and number theory. Since this date, other demonstrations by Klein [**30**] in 1895, Enriques [**17**] in 1900, Dickson [**14**] in 1914, etc., have appeared in more modern notation. Yet in the face of these conclusive proofs we still find a tremendous host advancing to the attack, armed only with straightedge and compasses. Some persistent stubbornness in our human race keeps this army at war-time strength and for each casualty there is at least one recruit ready to bear arms, indeed the same ones, in an effort to revise the scientific world and make it safe for the mathematician.

Once the virus of this fantastic disease gets into the brain, if proper antiseptics are not immediately applied, the victim begins a vicious circle that leads him from one outrage of logic to another. Consistently inconsistent, he slides under each fence, clears his conscience, and proceeds blithely to the next truth only to violate that in turn. It seems generally characteristic that all of these individuals have a superb command of flowery and bewitching language to tempt the uninitiated and gullible. To the professional mathematician, these phrases seem to serve but one purpose—to obscure the very violations that are always lurking in the proposals under one guise or another. These violations are at times very difficult to discover. But once brought to light, usually no amount of patient persuasion can convince the author of his error. Strangely enough, each new "solver" can see glaring mistakes in the work of his predecessor but is apparently oblivious to his own.

The fact that simple reasoning can accomplish nothing toward setting these people right has forced the professional mathematician to meet each proffered challenge in deep silence. The result, of course, in the already warped mind of the "savior of science" is the deep-rooted conviction that all mathematicans are in league against him. And that in itself becomes yet another unassailable argument of his infallibility. As a last resort, he turns to the layman through the medium of the daily newspapers much to the detriment of public faith in the professional mathematician.

Once a person has convinced himself that he has solved one of the Famous Problems that "have defied mathematicians for over two thousand years", it is but a short step to the realization that he is endowed with unusual powers. These powers are then focused upon all the other paradoxes from perpetual motion to the existence of God, and with characteristic consummate success. One professor of mathematics writes as follows:

> "Quite often I receive letters from some individual who has discovered a kinship between phenomena which to the benighted scientist appear worlds apart. One, possessed by a truly universal spirit, has succeeded in uniting into a single synthesis the Euclidean postulate of parallels and the quadrature of the circle, the Fermat problem and perpetual motion, the principle of relativity and the existence of the Deity, the quantum theory of the atom and the forecasts of the stock market, the abolition of wars, the solution of the economic depression and the liberation of mankind from the Bolshevist scourge—to mention but a few of the achievements he claims."

A typical person of this sort was Mr. L. S. B—. His self assurance was so great that he offered a thousand dollars to the one who would prove wrong his argument in support of the value 3 for π.

A very recent "solver" of the Trisection Problem announced his discovery to the editor of an American mathematical journal but refused to disclose the nature of the solution until he had been awarded the sum of $15,000. That amount, he said, was only the just compensation of an ordinary school teacher for services over the fifteen years that he had devoted to the problem—an amount that could very well come, he said, from football receipts.

CASE HISTORIES

1. *The Case of J. C. W—.*

In 1902 a little book, *Trisection of Angles* by Mr. W—, appeared with the explanatory preface:

> "... It was necessary to get outside of the problem to solve it, and it was not solved by a study or knowledge of Geometry or Trigonometry, as the author had never made a study of these branches of learning. The proof was arranged in Geometrical order and formula by Ada S. Flood.
>
> "The problem might have remained unsolved except for a study and analysis of the little poem, 'In the Distance', wherein the numbers 3 and 7

seem to coincide in various ways and wherein various other coincidences are demonstrated by the aid of progressive or triangular numbers. Herein was found the key to the solution of the problem:

"IN THE DISTANCE"

I

The countless legions passed away,
And all the hosts on earth to-day,
Like vanished dreams may be forgot,
Their names and deeds remembered not,
Their gilded glories gone;
Their works as rust and desert dust,
Fame's phantom shadows flown.

II

Or like enchanted music rung,
Our songs attuned to cadence sung,
Or names by mystic fate renowned,
By glamoured ancient glories crowned
With all that fame endears,
It nought would be to you or me,
Far down the distant years.

III

A few at most our troublous days;
Unto the vast unknown we gaze;
A glimmer of Immortal dawn,
A star of hope still shining on,
Gleams through the darkest sky;
A trust that good shall cross the flood,
And only evil die.

IV

Where doubt exists a hope may live;
None know the gifts that time may give;
Above our highest hopes and far
Beyong the dreamer's brightest star,
Have faith! for us may rise
The future's dawn, the shores unknown,
The fadeless Eden skies.

V

Let patience ever shield thy breast
From storm-tossed waves of wild unrest,
And love make all thy pathways bright,
Contentment make thy burdens light;
Let gloomy thoughts forlorn,
And griefs and fears, the pains and tears,
All pass like mists of morn.

VI

Haste not to leap the fabled stream;
What waits beyond we may not dream;
Rejoice to-day, yet meekly trust,
That only good above our dust,
By fate, somewhere, somehow,
From acts of ours may grow as flowers,
In far-off years from now.

VII

Trust now in fame now wealth to bless;
Go help the poor and soothe distress;
Be brave, be true and do your best;
Do good until with God you rest,
In some far wondrous home,
And all will be as well with thee,
Through all the years to come.

"*Coincidences*"

"... There are as many syllables to the verse as there are weeks to the year, and 52 punctuation marks are used in the 7 verses. There are 365 syllables in the 7 verses. Also, the second and fourth verses combined have 365 letters and fourth and sixth verses combined have 365 letters, corresponding to the number of days in one year... . The first letter of the alphabet is used as a word and for the commencement of words 33 times; 33 commas are used; there are 33 letters in the longest line and 33 lines preceding it. There are 24 letters in the last line and 24 letters in the first word of each verse combined; the sum of all numbers from 1 to 24 = 300, the number of words in the 7 verses... . The number of letters in the alphabet, 26, multiplied by the number of verses, 7, =182, the number of letters in the 7th verse... The most wonderful of all numbers is 1287. The number of verses, 7, multiplied by the number of letters 1287=9009: the answer reads the same either way backward or forward. The sum of all numbers from 1 to 1287=828828 which reads same either way... . The sum of all numbers from 1 to 7=28. 'God' is the 28th word of the 7th verse in the 4th line, and the 279th word of the work... . The sum of all numbers from 1 to 10=55: 'Mystic' is the 55th word of the work in the 10th line. Commencing with the Sun as 1, Mercury as 2, Venus 3, Earth 4, Mars 5, The Asteroids 6, Jupiter 7, Saturn 8, Uranus 9, Neptune 10, Comets 11, the Fixed Stars and Nebula 12, and 13th the Unknown: 13 multiplied by the number of verses, 13×7=91. 'Unknown' is the 91st word of the work... ."

Although Mr. W— lays considerable stress upon the poem and its numerical oddities, he fails to reveal its connection with the Trisection Problem. The error in his solution is the assumption that a certain arc in the construction is circular. This arc, however, was shown to be hyperbolic by Pappus in the 3rd Century. We need not enter into the details of the construction here.

2. *The Case of J. W—.*

Mr. W—, B. A., M. D., Edin., a native of Greenock, went to considerable pains and expense to publish in 1911 a magnificent book of 169 pages called *The Trisection of the Angle by Plane Geometry.* In the preface he calms the reader by assuring him that he need only understand the geometry of Euclid in order to digest his treatment. Unfortunately, Mr. W— labored under the delusion that calculations carried out to seven place accuracy were sufficient proof of his method. The editor of the Mathematical Gazette reviewed this book as follows:

"Dr. W— has found a formula for the third part of a given angle, and applies it to fifty selected cases... . This stately marshalling of the arithmetical procedure is worthy of a better cause than the computation of sines and cosines to seven figures... . He seems to be quite aware of the fact that the problem has been classed among those that are insoluble, and quotes from De Morgan to that effect. We fear that he may continue to hug his comfortable delusion in spite of all that can be said... ."

3. *The Case of J. J. C—.*

Mr. C—, president of an American university, published in 1931 the two works:

Euclid or Einstein. A Proof of the Parallel Theory and a Critique of Metageometry;

and

The Trisection of the Angle. The Trigonometric Functions of One-third of an Angle in Terms of the Functions of the Angle. The Insertion of Two Geometric Means Between a line and Another twice as Long. The Duplication of the Cube. Et al.

The first is a book of more than 300 pages which gives emphasis to the author's opening sentence:

> "We are surely living in a strange intellectual age."

In it Mr. C— "proves" the parallel postulate and concludes that the only geometry that can possibly exist is Euclidean. His attitude toward modern investigations is disclosed in the following quotations:

> "... This age has gone further in this respect than any other; it has extended its attacks to the utmost bounds of science. The mutineers against the old order have seized the ship of knowledge and nailed the flag of dissent to the mast; they have driven the defenders of all manner of orthodoxy below decks and battened down the hatches over them, and have left in their administration not a single department of science. ... When normally sound criticism turns into destructive bolshevism, it is time to inquire whether the criticism is as sound as that which it criticises."
>
> "As a result of this failure (to prove the parallel postulate), certain mathematicians of the last century came to the conclusion that the postulate was indemonstrable, certainly a very easy way to cut the Gordian knot of the difficulty; and then with the utmost inconsequence, and with more mental agility than either poise or balance, jumped to the other and much more radical and subversive conclusion, that the proposition itself was not valid."

This last is a misstatement. Mathematicians did not conclude that the postulate was invalid; they simply replaced it with another one which is consistent with the rest and upon this foundation created a vast and important non-Euclidean geometry.

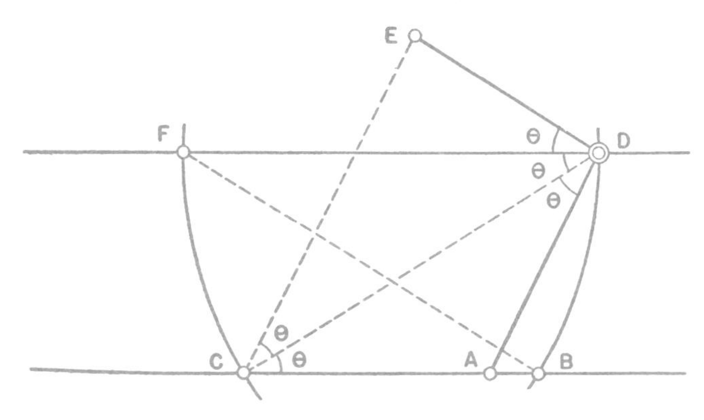

FIG. 40

The second work of Mr. C— disposes of the problem of Trisection. Because its absurdity is both simple and interesting we shall give the method here. The lines BC and DF are drawn parallel to each other.

With any point, such as D, as center, describe the circular arc FC. With the same radius and center F draw the arc DB. Construct the angle DCE equal to angle DCA. Draw DA parallel to EC and DE parallel to FB. Then DF and DC trisect angle ADE.

Nothing could be truer or more fundamentally sound. However, Mr. C— has his cart before the horse. Instead of trisecting a given angle, he has erected from an arbitrarily chosen angle DCA its *triple*, angle ADE. Due to the respected position that he held in the educational world, Mr. C— unfortunately received considerable notoriety for this bit of mathematical play. The newspapers of the day made much of his "discovery" and undoubtedly created excitement in the ranks of the layman.

A curious paragraph in the same pamphlet lists the trigonometric functions of one-third of an angle in terms of the angle:

$$\sin(A/3) = 2\sin A + \tan A; \qquad \cos(A/3) = 2\sec A + 1;$$

$$\tan(A/3) = 2\sin A; \qquad \sec(A/3) = 2\cos A + 1;$$

$$\cot(A/3) = 2\csc A; \qquad \csc(A/3) = 2\sin A + \cot A.$$

Using these formulas to calculate the functions of 30°, letting $A = 90°$, we find:

$$\sin 30° = \infty \qquad \cos 30° = \infty \qquad \tan 30° = 2$$

$$\sec 30° = 1 \qquad \csc 30° = 2 \qquad \cot 30° = 2.$$

This display seems doubly strange when we remember that the square of the sine added to the square of the cosine equals 1.

4. *The Case of J. J. G—.*

Mr. G—, onetime instructor of mathematics in a college of California, published in 1932 a beautiful little book under the title: *The Mathematical Atom.* That it struck a popular note among the interested public is evidenced by the fact that three editions appeared in scarcely more than a year's time. He recounts the "success" of his struggles with the Trisection Problem:

> "In the course of the attempt and upon closer scrutiny I found the *two lines* mathematicians had been in search of since the days of old Pythagoras securely linked up with a couple of sets of parallel lines crisscrossing each other and together forming 'perspectives of pleasant shades and wide open spaces';

and the two *distinguished points* nestling in the heart of two mutually overlapping right triangles, perched upon two tangents to a circle at the ends of two of its radii; and the *three great points O* and *A* and *B* dominating the whole expanse of the angle's empyrean."

Farther on, Mr. G— tells of his discovery of a new kind of triangle that seems to him destined to play a vital role on the mathematical stage:

"The *Golden Mean Triangle* will serve to show that even *the scalene triangle* is not to be classed among the lower host of things, 'the loose, the lawless, the exaggerated, the insolent, and the profane'. For though the scalene triangle may appear at a first glance to be something of a *sans-cullote,* and sartorially and æsthetically not quite on a par with the more aristocratic triangles, the capricious little vagabond can nevertheless be shown fundamentally and potentially to possess the properties of beauty and symmetry, even as it possesses the other metaphysical properties of truth and goodness,—which things are ontologically inherent in all of God's creations, yea, in their every tiniest atom or fragment, however humble or commonplace."

We need not comment upon these passages. It is regrettable that lack of space forces us to reject Mr. G—'s invitation to an excursion:

"... if you want to take a jaunt out into the belt of any angle, wide, narrow, or straight, and want to make equally good and spacious reservations for yourself and two companions, hitch your wagon to the twin stars—ALPHA and BETA GEMINORIUM; give them the reins, and they'll take you to see half a hundred points of interest on a tour through their vast domain, including a number of delightful stopovers at their own commanding coignes of vantage, leaving you—heart and fancy free—to walk and ramble about in the garden of the manor, *dolce far niente,* to your heart's content. Or to pause and invite your soul to rest... the while you hearken to the distant cosmic harmonies of the whirling spheres, as their echoes come crashing upon the treetops in diapasonic over- and under-tones, running through all the compass of the notes, symphonically blending with the rustling music of the forests, strummed out by fairy fingers upon a thousand harps of sunbeams piercing the fragrant shadows of the giant primeval groves."

Toward the latter part of the book we find Mr. G—'s method of "trisection": Describe the arc AB upon the given angle AOB. Draw lines OC bisecting the angle; and OD bisecting the half. The tangent to AB at E intersects OC at F. Draw FG parallel to OD. With F as center and FO as radius describe the arc cutting out the points D, G, C. Draw FD and EG which intersect each other at X. Then OX is the "trisecting" line.

We leave to the reader the fun of spotting the error in this method. As an approximation it is excellent.

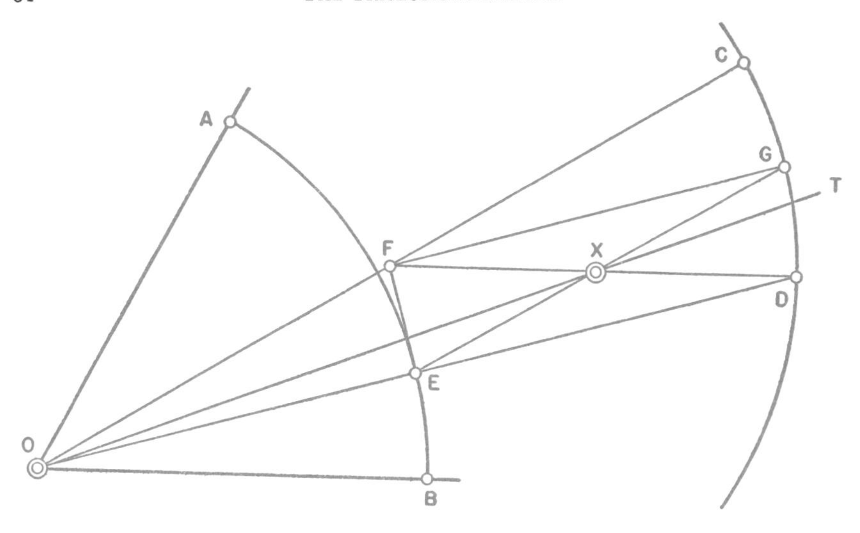

FIG. 41

5. *The Case of L. J. R. H—.*

It is an infrequent occurence that a purported straightedge and compasses trisection should appear in a serious periodical devoted to science. Through the editorial offices of every journal there passes a continual stream of new "solutions" which are either returned promptly to the authors or just as promptly consigned to rightful oblivion in the waste basket. Although every editor is constantly on guard, some of these attempts do slip through to the printed page. An instance of this is to be found in the paper: "A Solution for the Geometrical Trisection of Angles and the Proportional Dividing of Arcs" by L. J. R. H—. Mr. H— there gives two methods of "trisection", one of which follows:

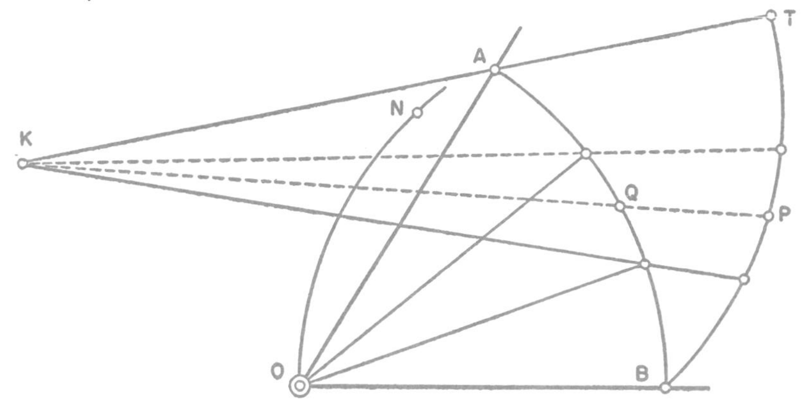

FIG. 42

Given the angle AOB. Draw an arc BA with center O. With the same radius and center B draw arc ON. With center at an arbitrary point N on ON, same radius, draw arc BT of any length and divide it into three equal arcs. Bisect arcs BA, BT to obtain the points P and Q. Draw the lines TA and PQ which intersect at K. Then lines drawn from K to the trisecting points of the arc BT "trisect" the arc BA.

It is easy to show that a fallacy exists and that the length of the arc BT and the position of the point N cannot be chosen at random. Thus, for example, if BT be taken as a semicircle the construction will yield the following "trisection" for 60°:

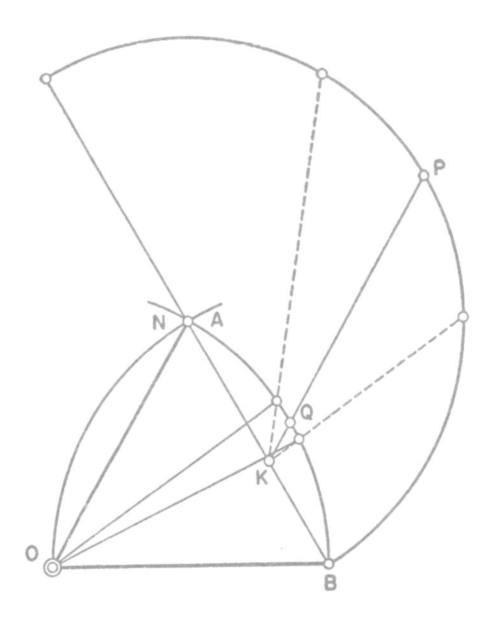

FIG. 43

This does not even appeal to the eye.

6. *Miscellaneous Cases*

1. *The Trisection of the Angle* by J. A. L—, (1890) ("being a problem in Geometry that has baffled the efforts of mathematicians up to the present day, now solved for the first time.")
2. *The Geometrical Problem Solved* by H. D. D—, (1892).
3. *Geometrical Division and Measurement of Arcs and Angles* by N. J—, (1900) ("the first person in the world to trisect, penta-

sect, and hepta-sect arcs and angles geometrically, or to measure arcs and angles without compass or protractor.").

4. *A New Method of Trisecting Any Angle and of Constructing a Regular Pentagon with Ruler and Compasses* by H. A. E—, Supt. of City Schools, Slater, Mo. (no date).
5. *Trisectio Arcus et Anguli* by J. W. Th. O—, (1906) ("...and hereby we give to the world the solution of this remarkable problem of twenty odd centuries. May the tired spirits of the past from Pytagoras and Euclid to Newton now rest in peace! We are happy ourselves at last to feel entitled to rest.")
6. *The Trisection of an Angle* by J. S—, (1914).
7. *Trisecting an Angle by Compass and Straightedge* by E. H. Y—, (1931).
8. *Euclidean Trisection, Quintisection, and Hexasection* by A. A. Z—, (1932).
9. *Solution of an Insolvable Problem* by B. D. H—, (1932).
10. *The Trisection of the Angle and Theorems and Corollaries Leading To It (Revised)* by F. S—, (1933).
11. *Trisecting an Angle of any General Magnitude* by L. A. McC— (1934).
12. *Youth Claims Formula Great Mathematicians Seek*, Associated Press Dispatch, (Aug. 31, 1935).

BIBLIOGRAPHY

1. Adler, A.: Theorie der geometrischen Konstruktionen, Leipzig, 1906.
2. Amadori: Trisezione d'un angolo qualunque mediante riga e compasso, Savona 1883.
3. Aubry: Journal de Mathématiques Spéciales, 1896, pp. 76-84; pp. 106-112.
4. Ball, W. W. R.: Mathematical Recreations and Essays, London, 1940.
5. Breidenbach, W.: Die Dreiteilung des Winkels, Leipzig, 1933.
6. Brennan, M. H.: The Trisection of the Arc, Devil's Lake, Dakota, 1888.
7. Brocard, H.: (a) Note sur la division mécanique de l'angle, Bull. Soc. Math. de France, III, 1875, pp. 47-48; V, 1876, pp. 43-47.
   (b) Notes de Bibliographie des Courbes Géométriques, 1897, p. 290.
8. Cajori, F.: A History of Mathematics, New York, 1926.
9. Ceva, Th.: Acta Erud., MDCXCV (1695), p. 290.
10. Dantzig, T.: Number, The Language of Science, New York, 1930.
11. De Morgan, A.: A Budget of Paradoxes, London. 1872.
12. Descartes, R.: La Géométrie, Paris, 1637, Berlin, 1894.
13. Dexter, O. P.: The Division of Angles, American News Co., New York, 1881.
14. Dickson, L. E.: Elementary Theory of Equations, New York, 1914.
15. Dürer, A.: Unterweysung der messung mit dem zirkel und richtscheyt, Nürnberg, 1525.
16. Edington, E. E.: House Bill No. 246, Indiana State Legislature, 1897, Proc. Indiana Academy of Science, 45, 1936, pp. 206-210.
17. Enriques, F.: Fragen der Elementargeometrie, II, Leipzig, 1911.
18. Ferguson, D. F.: Geometrical Construction for the Trisection of an Angle to any Required Degree of Accuracy, Mathematical Gazette, 9, 1919, p. 373.
19. Fialkowski: Teilung des Winkels und des Kreises, 1860, p. 11.
20. Genese, R. W.: On the Trisection of an Angle, Messenger of Mathematics, I, 1872, pp. 103, 181.
21. Givens, W. B.: The Division of Angles into Equal Parts and Polygon Construction, American Mathematical Monthly, XLV, 1938, pp. 653-656.
22. Good, A.: Scientific Amusements, (no date: reprinted about 1937).
23. Heath, T. L.: Greek Mathematics, Oxford, 1921.
24. Hilbert, D.: The Foundations of Geometry, Chicago, 1902.
25. Hippauf, H.: Lösung des Problems der Trisection, Leipzig, 1872.
26. Hudson, H. P.: Ruler and Compasses, London, 1916.
27. Hutton: Philosophical Recreations, 1844.
28. Juredini, G. M.: A New Curve Connected with Two Classical Problems, American Mathematical Monthly, 33, 1926, p. 377 ff.

29. Kempe, A. B.: (a) Messenger of Mathematics, NS IV, 1875, pp. 121-124.
(b) How to Draw a Straight Line, New York, 1877.

30. Klein, F.: Famous Problems of Elementary Geometry, Boston, 1897.

31. Kortum, H.: Uber geometrische Aufgaben dritten und vierten Grades, Bonn, 1869.

32. Lagarrique, J. F.: The Trisection Compass, New York, 1831.

33. Laisant, C. A.: Note sur un Compas Trisecteur, Compte rendu (Congres de Nantes), 1875, pp. 61-63.

34. Lucy, A. W.: (a) A Method of Trisecting an Angle, Mathematical Gazette, 11, 1922, p. 21.
(b) To Divide an Angle into any Number of Equal Parts, Mathematical Gazette, 14, 1928, pp. 137-138.

35. Mitzscherling, A.: Das Problem der Kreisteilung, Leipzig, 1913.

36. Montucla: Histoire des recherches sur la Quadrature du Cercle, Paris, 1831.

37. Nicolson, T. W.: The Multisection of Angles, The Analyst, X, 1883, pp. 41-43.

38. Ocagne, M. d': Etude rationelle du Probleme de la Trisection de l'Angle, L'Enseignment Math., 1934, pp. 49-63.

39. Pappus: Coll. Math., Prob. VIII, Prop. XXXII.

40. Perron, O.: Sitzungsberichte der Bayerischen Academie der Wissenschaften, 1933, pp. 439 ff., 1929, pp 341 ff.

41. Priestley, H. J.: Duplication, Trisection and Elliptical Compasses, Mathematical Gazette, 12, 1924, pp. 212-216.

42. Schubert, H. C. H.: Mathematical Essays and Recreations, Chicago, 1917

43. Scientific American, July, 1933; April, 1936, pp. 190-191; 228-229.

44. Scudder, H. T.: How to Trisect an Angle with a Carpenter's Square, American Mathematical Monthly, 1928, pp. 250-251

45. Sidler, G.: Zur Dreiteilung eines Kreisbogens, Bern, 1876.

46. Smith, J. C.: Ann. di Mat., 3, 1869, p. 112; Collected Math. papers 2, p. 1.

47. Sylvester, J. J.: Collected Works.

48 Tropfke: Geschichte der Elementar-Mathematik, Leipzig, 1930

49. Vahlen, T.: Konstruktionen und Approximationen, Leipzig, 1911

50. Wulff-Parchim, L.. Dürer als Mathematiker, 1928.

51. Yates, R. C.: (a) A Trisector, National Mathematics Magazine, XII, 1938, pp. 323-324.
(b) Line Motion and Trisection, Ibid., XIII, 1938, pp. 1-4.
(c) The Angle Ruler, the Marked Ruler, and the Carpenters' Square, Ibid., XV, 1940, pp. 61-73.

52. For a general bibliography, see the supplements to L'Intermédiaire des Mathématiciens, Paris, May and June, 1904.